THE NEXT
HUNDRED YEARS

ALSO BY HARRISON BROWN

The Challenge of Man's Future

Man's Natural and Technological Resources

THE NEXT HUNDRED YEARS

A Discussion Prepared for Leaders of American Industry

by
Harrison Brown, James Bonner, John Weir
of the California Institute of Technology

THE VIKING PRESS · NEW YORK

261 323

One

SOME QUESTIONS

In this dynamic nation of ours, where things happen so quickly, where situations are changing at an ever accelerating tempo, it is extremely easy for us to lose perspective. In our worrying about today we tend to forget the problems of tomorrow. And in our fretting about how today differs from yesterday, some of us somehow look back on yesterday as being "normal." Actually there has obviously been no such thing as normality during the last three centuries for the simple reason that there has been such steady and rapid change during the entire period.

This is a fact which apparently escapes many persons. Many of us are constantly looking to the past, dreaming of it, wishing for it, not realizing that if we were to succeed in taking ourselves back to the period when there was little change from one generation to the next we would have to return to the Middle Ages—back to the days of the Black Death, of hopeless malnutrition and superstition, of ignorance and tyranny.

During the last three hundred years man has achieved a degree of power over his environment which is unprecedented in the thousands of years of human history which preceded them and in the hundreds of thousands of years of human prehistory. Our rate of material progress and our rate of growth seem to be steadily accelerating, and one cannot help asking, For how long can this acceleration and this growth continue? Will we continue to accelerate? Will we level off? Could it be that, perhaps without realizing it, we are painting ourselves into a corner? Could it even be that we are headed toward catastrophe?

What is the future of our industrial civilization likely to be? Can we foresee the major problems that will confront us? Are these problems soluble? What kind of society could our science and our technology help us to create in a world at peace?

These are questions the answers to which, in the long run, will determine whether our culture, our nation, our children, live or die. Few persons have posed them, and even fewer have made any serious attempt to answer them.

In this study we would like to take what we call "the long view" and attempt to make an assessment of the future of our scientific-technological-industrial civilization. We believe that it is important to look thus into the future, since it is only by study of what may happen in the years ahead that society can properly plan its affairs. Only by assessing the future as well as we are able can we prepare ourselves for the trip forward.

To us "the long view" seems particularly important because it can help us to leave our children a world at least as habitable as that which we inherited from our parents. And the precedents which we set will have their effect upon the welfare of our children's children. Indeed, the destiny of the human species is being determined in large part by the actions and inactions of those of us who are alive today.

FOREWORD TO THE COMPASS EDITION

The chief pleasure of a forecaster of future events lies in finding that his predictions are correct; that he has properly weighed trends and limits and has in fact foreseen the future. We feel a little of such pleasure. Not of course that a full hundred years of human history have validated the prognoses which we set down some years ago in this book, but that sufficient time has gone by to make clear that the trends which we visualized as critical for the development of a technical-industrial civilization are taking place. Indeed, where we have erred it has generally been in the direction of underestimation. Thus the shortage of our world-wide resources of technically skilled manpower is developing even more rapidly than foreseen by us in this volume. Industrialization of underdeveloped countries is progressing more slowly than we had visualized. The pressing problem of increasing world food output is proving to be even more difficult than we predicted. Finally, our projections of population growth now seem very conservative. The pressure of a continuing rapid increase in human numbers makes solutions to the problems discussed in *The Next Hundred Years* even more urgently to be desired.

The principal task of this book is to inquire into the limits which must ultimately bound the development of our industrial society and the problems which must be faced as we approach these limits. These limits and the associated problems appear to us to be as clear and real today as they were when the present work was first written. We commend the reader to their study.

Pasadena, California
March 1963

H. B., J. B., J. W.

ACKNOWLEDGMENTS

The concept of presenting symposia on resources and population problems for industry originated with Robert V. Bartz. We are indebted to Mr. Bartz for his bold concept, for his careful arrangements, for his valuable constructive suggestions, and for his continuing friendly support.

We wish to thank our colleagues at the California Institute of Technology for their help and suggestions while these conferences were in preparation. And we acknowledge our indebtedness to our industrial friends, from whom we have learned so much during the past year.

We are greatly indebted to Elspeth Highkin for her work during the preparation of these conferences, and to Barbara Dixon for her preparation of the figures. We acknowledge with thanks the help of Barbara Brown, Fay Miko, Dianne Stephens, and Florence Wiltse in the preparation of the manuscript. We are indebted to M. King Hubbert for Figures 16, 17, and 20 (see Bibliography).

PREFACE

by

Lee A. DuBridge

President of the California Institute of Technology

There are few things that are more difficult for most of us to do than to look into the future. We can make our plans for next week or next month or even for the next fiscal year. But to peer five or ten years into the future, much less fifty to a hundred years, requires an exercise of imagination which is difficult at best—and in most cases out of the question. There is little time for such imaginings, and their practical value, attended by uncertainties as they are, seems remote.

Forecasts of the future have nonetheless an attraction for all of us. Our curiosity, if nothing else, encourages us to inquire into the shape of things to come. This is the only way we have of experiencing a future beyond our own life span.

The modern corporation, as contrasted with an individual, is a long-lived entity. A successful corporation will, it can be hoped, still be in existence one hundred years hence, after all its existing personnel—and indeed their children and grandchildren too—have gone. Yet it is becoming increasingly evident that the success of a corporation and the success of a nation, a century hence, will depend on what it is doing today. Therefore an increasing interest is to be found among corporation executives in trying to peer into the future and to ask how company policies today can best be adapted to potential future developments.

No one can pretend, of course, that it is possible to foretell the future with any precision for even a year ahead. New inventions, new political developments at home or abroad are more than likely to invalidate such predictions and frustrate the would-be prophet.

Yet certain long-term trends can be perceived in many fields, and reasonably certain projections can be evolved. We cannot foresee the precise kinds of machines that men will be using twenty-five or fifty or a hundred years hence. (Think of how wrong any forecast made in 1857 would certainly have turned out to be!) But we can be rather certain that men will be using *energy* in ever increasing amounts as the years go by. To examine the sources of energy which seem to be ultimately available on this planet is thus a valuable and feasible project. It is also important to examine the earth's resources of iron, copper, aluminum, and other materials and to inquire into the future adequacy of these supplies.

That long-range considerations of the earth's resources should be of interest and importance to our industrial leaders first occurred to Mr. Robert V. Bartz, Director of the Industrial Associates program at the California Institute of Technology. Under his stimulus a group of faculty members gathered together to explore and discuss these matters, first among themselves, and later with corporate executives. Harrison Brown, Professor of Geochemistry, whose book *The Challenge of Man's Future* had already examined some of the issues, undertook the consideration of the spread and intensification of our industrial culture.

It is evident, however, that material resources bound up with human resources and vice versa are significant only in relation to the number of people using them. The problems of world population and of how this population is to be fed were therefore considered by James Bonner, Professor of Biology.

Finally it was realized that the question of what constitutes a resource is really the question of how intelligently man uses the materials with which the earth is endowed and of how successfully he discovers new ways of using these materials. Intellectual rather than physical resources may eventually limit man's material progress. John Weir, Professor of Psychology, analyzed the intellectual resources of the world from the standpoint of its ability to produce creative solutions to technical problems.

The group prepared an outline of their thinking on these problems and proceeded to present their questions and ideas to meetings of executives of certain major corporations. The interest was intense and, even though most executives had not previously given these long-term problems very concerted attention, there were many who had valuable ideas and information to offer. Some thirty conferences were held with individual company groups, each conference lasting for several hours, and each confined to the top executives of the corporation.

This book is a summary—a distillate, perhaps—of these conferences. Their value and interest exceeded all expectations and led to an insistent demand that the material be made publicly available. It is hoped that this publication will stimulate further discussions of matters pertaining to resources, important as they are to the future of our nation and of the world. We trust also that this publication will serve as evidence that members of university and industrial staffs can profitably cooperate in examining many types of problems of importance to human welfare.

CONTENTS

CONTENTS

THE NEXT
HUNDRED YEARS

Two

ON FORECASTING THE FUTURE

This study, then, is essentially an effort to forecast the future of our scientific-technological-industrial civilization. We use the term "forecast" rather than "prophesy," for, like Sir Charles Galton Darwin, we wish to stress that any estimate of the future of anything as complicated as human society must be in essence an assessment of relative probabilities. Darwin uses the analogy of the meteorologist attempting to forecast the future pattern of weather. By putting together all available information concerning the weather in various parts of the world, and by applying his knowledge of the patterns of weather behavior under similar circumstances in the past, he ventures to forecast the *probabilities* of weather behavior in the future. He does so while recognizing that there are many things he does not know.

So, recognizing fully that there are a great many things we do not know concerning human society and its environment, we can nevertheless put together the available information concerning its status in various parts of the world today, and by applying our knowledge of the patterns of change in the past we can forecast the *probabilities* of various patterns in the future.

We know that the meteorologist is frequently "wrong" in the sense that many of the events judged by him to be the most probable do not come to pass. In like manner, forecasts of the future state of the world can be wrong. And in the latter case we must further consider the effect of the forecast upon the ultimate outcome. Whereas the forecast of weather by the meteorologist has no effect upon the weather, widespread recognition of the probabilities concerning the future state of mankind can in itself alter those probabilities. If a danger can be foreseen, steps can be taken to forestall it.

The first major attempt to assess the future condition of mankind on the basis of available scientific evidence was made over one hundred and fifty years ago by Malthus. Surveying the poverty in early industrial England, Malthus reached the conclusion that the situation would become worse with time, since "the power of population is indefinitely greater than the power of the earth to produce subsistence for man." He reasoned that the number of people living on the earth is necessarily limited by the means of subsistence and that it invariably increases where the means of subsistence increase, unless prevented by some very powerful checks. He pointed out that population tends to multiply in "geometric ratio," by which he meant (to oversimplify) that each succeeding generation would be very much larger than the one which preceded it. It seemed evident to Malthus, however, that the means of subsistence could not be increased as rapidly as that. At the time the only effective means of increasing food production was to bring more land under cultivation. Already a large part of the English soil was cultivated, and it seemed certain that new land could not be brought under the plows in "geometric ratio."

Had Malthus made his forecast at a time in history less favorable to an increase in human welfare, his arguments would have been substantiated rather firmly by events and he probably would have gone down in history as a great prophet. Instead, for well over a century following the publication of his theory, the economic condition of the average Englishman, far from becoming worse with each succeeding year, improved with breathtaking rapidity. The condition of man in nineteenth- and twentieth-century England so belied the Malthusian theory that the theory itself has now fallen into disrepute and is usually mentioned only as an example of a forecast that was quickly proved wrong. Indeed, it is frequently cited, more often by economists than by scientists and engineers, as an argument for discounting modern attempts to forecast the future condition of mankind, particularly if the view expressed is a gloomy one.

When we look back upon Malthus and his times it becomes clear that his major errors stemmed not from faulty reasoning but from insufficient knowledge. Within the framework of the information available to him, his forecasts of food shortage and poverty were reasonable. But he failed to foresee the extent to which England would in effect extend her agricultural resources by trading the products of her industries for the farm products of Canada, Australia, and New Zealand, and to realize how improved technology would increase both industrial and agricultural output per man-hour and agricultural yields per acre and improve public health and welfare. And, without foreknowledge of the improved standards of living which were in the making, he could not foresee that these would bring about a decrease in birth rates.

Today we have at least a reasonable chance of forecasting more accurately than did Malthus. For one thing, we know more than he did about the extent, the potentialities, and the limitations of the world in which we live. For another, we know more about both the potentialities and the limitations of our technology.

The forecasts in this study are based in part upon the premise that any technological advance is possible, provided that the fundamental physical and biological laws that govern the world in which we live are not violated. This means, for example, that we discount perpetual motion. But it means as well that we are taking into consideration a wide range of technological advances, some of which are foreseeable and some of which are so far removed from even advanced technical experience that they can be visualized only dimly.

Malthus failed to appreciate the importance of the world outside England as a source of both food and raw materials. In this study we have attempted to take into account not only the limitations of our own world but the limitations of the solar system as well. Even were we to have inexpensive and safe interplanetary flight, the resources of the planet Earth would not be appreciably augmented. On the basis of what we now know about the compositions and structures of the other planets, there is little hope that we can look outside the earth (except, of course, to the sun as a source of energy) for any appreciable fraction of our sustenance.

The reader should keep in mind above all else that we are in what Sir Charles Darwin calls an "abnormal situation"—a period of rapid transition from a culture which has been predominantly agrarian to one which is predominantly industrial. Like Malthus, we suffer from the handicap of forecasting during a period of abnormally rapid change. And, as was true of him, had we made a forecast at almost any time in the past, or perhaps were we writing at practically any time in the future, our chances of being correct would be considerably greater than they are today.

Thermodynamics, the great branch of science which tells us what can and what cannot happen in the physical world, enables us to predict stable conditions in physical systems with a high degree of accuracy. But it tells us nothing about rates—it tells us nothing about the rapidity with which a stable condition may be approached.

In like manner we are able to outline, we believe with a considerable degree of accuracy, the conditions for a stable, highly industrialized world. But the kinetics of the approach to that condition are extremely complicated, and, since they depend upon many human variables, the forecasting of rates of change is an extremely hazardous undertaking.

We nevertheless can set limits to the possible rates of change of human culture. One obvious limit is zero—a rate of change which has been approximated by human culture during the greater part of man's existence. Another and upper limit, at least in the past although not necessarily in the future, is determined by the length of a human generation—the average span of time between the birth of an individual and the birth of his offspring. In general, perhaps always, major cultural changes have taken place in human society on a time scale measured in human generations. This limit has resulted in part from the fact that patterns of culture are crystallized in the individual at a very early age, so that a new, more flexible generation is required to accept a major innovation and to incorporate it into its culture.

As we shall see, one of the major problems confronting mankind today is that of time scale in relation to social and cultural change. Is there something fundamentally fixed about the time span of a generation? Or are there ways by which human ingenuity can change it so that social and cultural patterns can be modified with dramatic suddenness? If such ways were to be discovered, the rates of change we foresee might be exceeded, and the time required to attain our final stable society would be shortened.

Three

SOME CONTRASTS

Among the 2600 million or so human beings who inhabit the earth
there are enormous differences in ways of life (some of which are
illustrated in Figures 1A and 1B). At one end of the economic
scale we find the people of the United States, representing but
6 per cent of the world's population, able, largely as the result of
the high level of industrialization and the abundant resources with
which the land was originally endowed, to consume about 50
per cent of the goods produced in the world. We are well fed—
perhaps too well fed. Each person on the average consumes food
with an energy content of more than 3100 calories each day, a
daily caloric intake which is nearly twice that of the average inhabitant of India. Indeed, fewer than 10 per cent of the inhabitants
of our planet are able to live on a standard of food-intake equivalent
to that enjoyed by the average American.

Although we have only 6 per cent of the world's population,
we produce 15 per cent of the world's potential food calories, twice
the daily production of potential food in all India. Further, we are
able to eat a diet which not only is calorically adequate but which
also provides in abundance expensive and nutritive animal products.
Without these our food would seem to us to be lacking both nutritionally and gastronomically—though, nutritionally speaking, we
could do equally well by substituting vegetable calories for many

but not all of the animal calories we now eat. By contrast, the people of India are restricted to a much leaner diet, which furthermore contains only one-fifth of the animal calories per capita which we consume.

On the material side, we in the United States have an automobile and a telephone for approximately every three persons. We own radios and television sets, refrigerators and washing machines, cameras and wristwatches, toilets and bathtubs. Our gross national product per capita is two and one-half times larger than that of the United Kingdom, nearly eleven times larger than that of Japan and nearly a hundred times larger than that of India. When we add up all the steel which is in use in our society in the form of machines, automobiles, railroads, and the multiplicity of other artifacts in our daily lives, we find that we have in use about nine tons of steel per person, as contrasted with only a few pounds per person in India. Our annual production of steel per capita is about thirteen hundred pounds, compared with about seven hundred pounds in the United Kingdom, one hundred and seventy-five pounds in Japan, and little more than seven pounds per person in India. Our electrical consumption per capita is about twice that of the United Kingdom, nearly five times that of Japan, and nearly a hundred times that of India.

At the opposite end of the economic scale we find the vast populations which dwell in the greater part of Asia, in parts of Africa, in all of Central America, and in parts of South America. Fully 50 per cent of the world's population lives under conditions of extreme poverty with food supplies far less than the minimum required for a healthy existence, and misery and privation the rule rather than the exception. These conditions have, at least until recently, been taken for granted.

This great range in the amount of food and material resources available to different peoples of the world is also found in the case of the less tangible necessities of modern life, such as health and education. In a country such as India, where nutrition is at a near-starvation level, where there are 6000 people for every physician

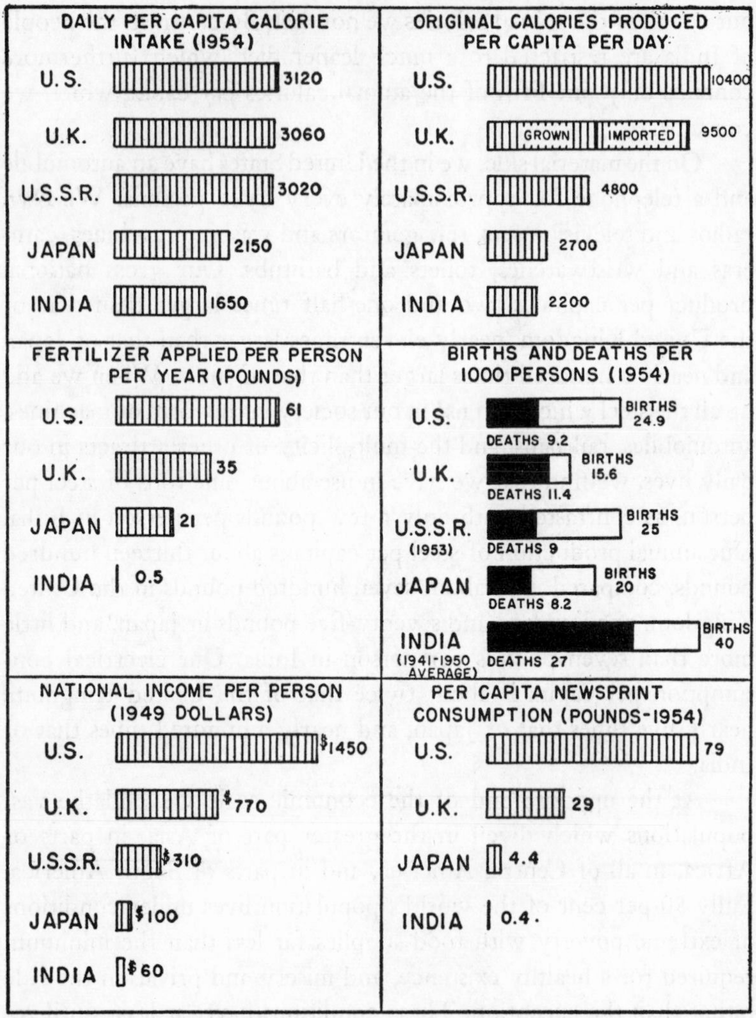

FIGURE 1 A

and 2400 people for every hospital bed, death rates are high. The chances of dying prematurely are much less in the United States, where there is a physician for every 750 persons and a hospital bed

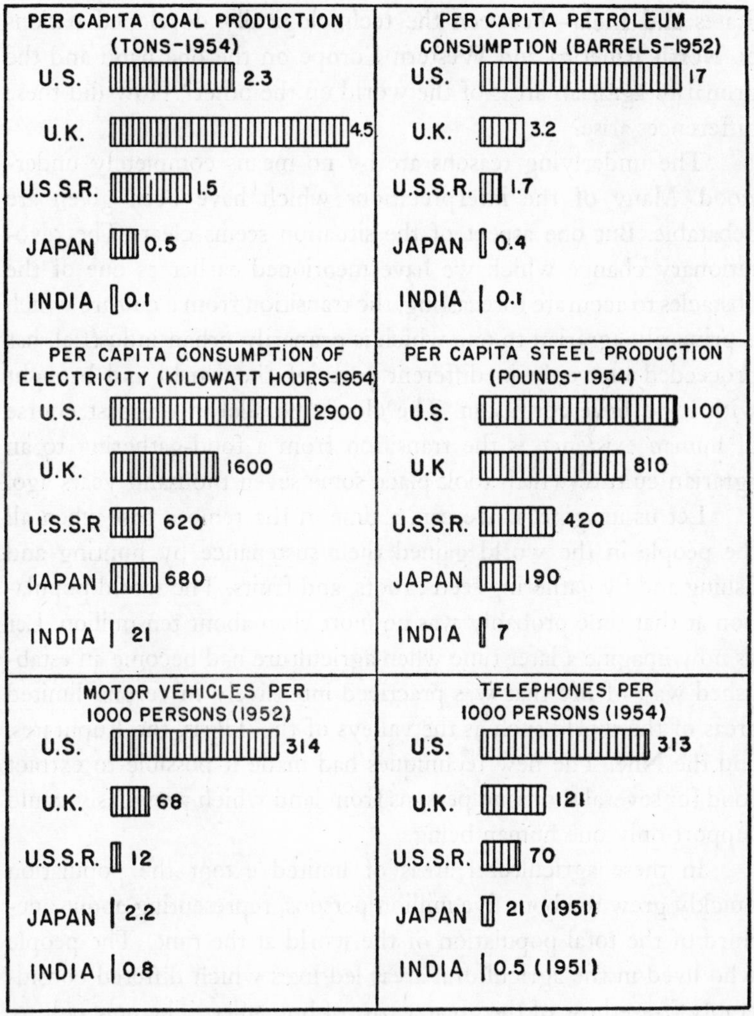

PER CAPITA COAL PRODUCTION (TONS–1954)	PER CAPITA PETROLEUM CONSUMPTION (BARRELS–1952)
U.S. 2.3	U.S. 17
U.K. 4.5	U.K. 3.2
U.S.S.R. 1.5	U.S.S.R. 1.7
JAPAN 0.5	JAPAN 0.4
INDIA 0.1	INDIA 0.1
PER CAPITA CONSUMPTION OF ELECTRICITY (KILOWATT HOURS–1954)	PER CAPITA STEEL PRODUCTION (POUNDS–1954)
U.S. 2900	U.S. 1100
U.K. 1600	U.K 810
U.S.S.R 620	U.S.S.R. 420
JAPAN 680	JAPAN 190
INDIA 21	INDIA 7
MOTOR VEHICLES PER 1000 PERSONS (1952)	TELEPHONES PER 1000 PERSONS (1954)
U.S. 314	U.S. 313
U.K. 68	U.K. 121
U.S.S.R. 12	U.S.S.R. 70
JAPAN 2.2	JAPAN 21 (1951)
INDIA 0.8	INDIA 0.5 (1951)

FIGURE 1 B

for every 110, and where education and technology combine to sustain effective public-health services.

Why do we find these enormous contrasts between the United

States and India—between the technologically developed nations of North America and Western Europe on the one hand and the primarily agrarian areas of the world on the other? How did these differences arise?

The underlying reasons are by no means completely understood. Many of the interpretations which have been given are debatable. But one aspect of the situation seems clear. The revolutionary change which we have mentioned earlier as one of the obstacles to accurate forecasting, the transition from a culture which is primarily agrarian to one which is primarily urban-industrial, has proceeded unevenly in different parts of the world and brought with it no little confusion. The closest parallel in the past course of human existence is the transition from a food-gathering to an agrarian culture which took place some seven thousand years ago.

Let us imagine, if we can, a time in the remote past when all the people in the world gained their sustenance by hunting and fishing and by gathering seeds, roots, and fruits. The world population at that time probably was no more than about ten million. Let us now imagine a later time when agriculture had become an established way of life that was practiced intensively in certain limited areas of the world such as the valleys of the Tigris, the Euphrates, and the Nile. The new techniques had made it possible to extract food for several thousand persons from land which previously could support only one human being.

In these agricultural areas of limited extent the population quickly grew to about five million persons, representing about one-third of the total population of the world at the time. The people who lived in the agricultural areas led lives which differed considerably from those of the greater part of humanity. The new culture permitted them to live in relative comfort in villages and cities. The ease with which food could be obtained led to unprecedented good health, which in turn led to an unprecedented rate of population growth.

By contrast, the people of the old food-gathering culture, representing the greater part of humanity, had saturated the land. Their population had grown to the maximum that could be provided for, in consideration of the techniques which were available to them, with the result that malnutrition and disease were widespread and famines were an all too familiar occurrence.

The situation which existed in the world at this remote time was similar in many respects to that which prevails in the world today. The contrasts which then existed between the wealthy agricultural minority and the poverty-stricken food-gathering majority are paralleled today by the contrasts between the wealthy industrialized minority and the poverty-stricken agricultural majority. Then the techniques of agriculture spread from one region to another, eventually to become world-wide. Today the techniques of industry are spreading from region to region, and it seems likely that, barring a world catastrophe, they too will become world-wide.

The spread of the agricultural revolution reached its eventual limit as the world's arable land became settled. As agriculture requires land, so industry requires huge quantities of raw materials —ores of iron, copper, aluminum, and a variety of other metals; quantities of non-metals such as sulphur, phosphate rock, and water; adequate sources of energy such as coal, petroleum, and water power. To what degree can we expect the longevity of industrial civilization and the extent to which it spreads to be limited by the availability of these raw materials?

The factors which will determine the future supply of and demand for raw materials are numerous. In attempting to assess them, we can divide the broad question into several component parts. First we must inquire into the increasing per capita demands for raw materials in highly industrialized societies. Within the United States, for example, these have increased steadily during the course of the last century. With each new year more raw materials are required to support an individual within our society than were required the year before. For how long a time can we expect this trend to continue? Is there any foreseeable limit to the per capita requirements for raw materials within a highly industrialized society?

The second factor concerns the rate of spread of industrial civilization. During the course of the last three hundred years we have seen industrialization emerge in Western Europe and jump the Atlantic Ocean to the United States. More recently it has come to dominate Japan and the Soviet Union. Today we hear rumblings of impending industrialization in India, in China, in parts of Africa, and in parts of South America. How quickly can we expect this process to take place? How rapidly can we expect the per capita demands for raw material in these at present under-developed areas to increase? And as they increase, are there sufficient raw materials in the world to satisfy, in such areas as India and China, demands which approach even remotely those which are now characteristic of the nations of the West?

Third, we must ask how large the population of human beings in the world is likely to become. Knowing the per capita demands for raw materials in the various regions of the world, by how many people must we multiply in order to determine the total drain upon the earth's resources? In order to determine this we must assess the number of people that we can feed.

The fourth factor is concerned with the amounts of raw materials available to man. What is a usable raw material? Certainly during the course of the last few decades we have seen our concepts changed drastically. Today, largely as a result of the application of our accumulated scientific knowledge, we are processing much leaner ores than were processed a few years ago, and we are using materials which were then undreamed of. As a result of this experience our concept of a raw material has constantly broadened.

How much can it continue to expand? Clearly this will depend upon the rate with which new knowledge can be accumulated and applied. And this in turn will depend upon the extent to which we are able to develop our human-resource potential.

Four

DEMANDS FOR RAW MATERIALS
IN AN INDUSTRIAL SOCIETY

During the greater part of man's history and his prehistory his demands for raw materials have been modest. During the hundreds of thousands of years which passed while man lived a food-gathering existence his dietary needs were confined to the fruits which he picked, the roots which he dug, and the animals which he was able to kill. When he found that he could control, and thus use, fire, his requirements increased, and many millennia ago he reached the point at which he consumed more energy in his fires than in his food, and the need for fuel was added to that for food. When his ingenuity stimulated him to shape tools from stone, he looked to the earth for certain types of stone which were better than others. When he took the tremendous step forward represented by the shift from stone tools to copper tools, copper deposits were avidly sought throughout the then known world. When he learned how to extract metallic iron from its ores, iron ore and wood suitable for conversion to charcoal came to be looked upon as necessary to survival. Bit by bit, man's demands for raw materials were increasing, and hitherto undreamed of "luxuries" were becoming "necessities."

During the rise of the great ancient urban cultures, demands for raw materials, particularly wood fuel, clay, stone, and ores of copper and tin reached very high levels. But they now seem small when compared with the needs precipitated by the Industrial Revolution, which linked coal to iron and found ways to convert heat into mechanical and electrical energy. During the three centuries in which the industrial giant has been growing, both the demand and the rate of increase of the demand for raw materials have risen and still are rising in a fantastic spiral.

England was the first area of the world to adopt an economy based on coal, iron, and mechanical power. As early as the year 1700 coal was being burned at an annual rate of ⅓ ton per person. By the turn of the nineteenth century per capita consumption exceeded ½ ton of coal and 36 pounds of iron per year. By the year 1850 this had risen to 1 ton of coal and 175 pounds of new iron per person per year, and by the beginning of the twentieth century to 5 tons of coal and 440 pounds of iron.

The industrialization of the New World lagged behind that of England by about thirty years. In 1880, for example, per capita production of pig iron in the United States was approximately that attained in England by 1850. Following this lag, however, the iron-and-steel industry grew extremely rapidly in the United States, so that by the year 1900 our annual per capita production of pig iron very nearly equaled that of the United Kingdom, and during the first half of the twentieth century more than doubled, approaching 1000 pounds per person in 1955.

We have now reached the point at which enormous quantities of raw materials are required to support a single individual within a highly industrialized society such as that in the United States. We require and produce each year, for each person, about 1300 pounds of steel, 23 pounds of copper, and 16 pounds of lead, in addition to considerable quantities of other metals.

Our demands for non-metals are even more impressive. Each year, for every person in our country, over 3.5 tons of stone, sand, and gravel must be dug from the earth, transported, and used in one way or another. Each of us uses, directly or indirectly, every year, over 500 pounds of cement, nearly 400 pounds of clay, over 200 pounds of common salt, and over 100 pounds of phosphate rock. Altogether, over 20 tons of raw materials must be dug from the earth and processed each year in order to support a single individual in our society. And these amounts are steadily increasing.

Each year large quantities of metals are lost irrecoverably as the result of corrosion, inefficiencies in handling, and physical dissemination. A part of the annual production of new metal serves the purpose of making up for these losses. But in the cases of most metals, production has exceeded losses and there has been a steady net gain in the quantity in actual use.

Between 5 billion and 6 billion tons of iron have been produced in the world since the beginning of its manufacture, or over 2 tons for every human being now living. But in the United States alone about 2.3 billion tons have been produced since 1850, or about 14 tons for every present inhabitant of the country.

Only a fraction of the iron which has been produced is still in use, for a variety of losses have taken their toll, and it is impossible ever to perpetuate all the metal originally manufactured, even when scrap is skillfully reprocessed for re-use. Ships are sunk and never recovered; objects rust; the gradual attrition of moving parts of machines brings about loss. And even when obsolete machines, structural steel beams, and other discarded masses of iron and steel are recovered as scrap there is a 10-per-cent loss involved in producing new steel from old. Thus of the 5 to 6 billion tons of iron which have been produced in the world, about 35 per cent has been lost, never to be recovered, leaving in use about 3.5 billion tons, corresponding to about 1.5 tons per human being. Of the 2.3 billion tons of iron which have been produced in the United States, about 1.5 billion tons are still in use in the form of automobiles, trucks, trains, rails, structural steel, machinery, nails, screws and wires, and a host of other objects. This amount corresponds to about 9 tons per person.

Although iron is the most widely used metal in our society, we need a variety of other metals in smaller but nevertheless substantial quantities: copper is needed for its electrical or thermal conductivity and for other uses in which a high degree of resistance to corrosion is desirable; zinc, for protective coatings and for dry cells; lead, for storage batteries, in construction, and as an ingredient in gasoline anti-knock agents; tin, as a protective coating and as an essential ingredient in several low-melting-point alloys. The list of essential metals, each of which possesses a unique combination of physical and chemical properties, is a long one.

Although the use of all metals and the rate of increase of their use have risen steadily during the last fifty years, the ratios of amounts of various metals used have remained remarkably constant, with a very few notable exceptions. In spite of the fact that demands for both copper and steel have increased more than tenfold during this time, the ratio of the consumption of the two metals has changed very little—from 36 pounds of copper per ton of steel in 1900 to 42 pounds of copper per ton of steel in 1950, with an average of 39 pounds of copper to a ton of steel. Similarly there has been surprisingly little change in the proportions of most other metals. Our demands for lead have averaged about 37 pounds per ton of steel produced. Zinc demands have averaged 27 pounds, and demands for tin somewhat over 4 pounds per ton of steel. Of course new discoveries and new technological developments have produced rapidly changing situations in the cases of the light metals—notably aluminum, magnesium, and titanium—and in the special cases of uranium and thorium.

It can be seen that the per capita quantities of metals other than steel which are in use in the United States amount to many hundreds of pounds. For every person in our country there are probably in existence over 300 pounds of copper, at least 100 pounds of lead, and about 200 pounds of zinc. There are probably between 5 and 10 pounds of tin in soldered joints alone, for every person.

We have seen that the quantities of materials which must be in existence in order to support an individual in a highly industrialized society have increased steadily. To what extent can we expect them to increase in the future? Can we expect the curves of quantities of materials per capita to taper off? Or will they continue to rise for an indefinitely long period of time?

It seems clear that the per capita quantities of materials needed will probably continue to rise for the obvious reason that it is un-

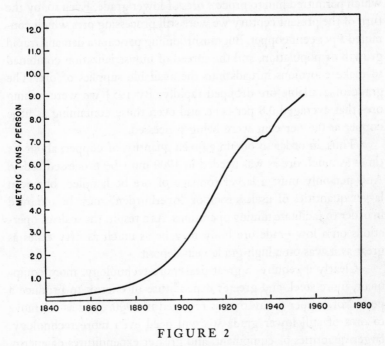

FIGURE 2

Estimated Quantity of Steel per Capita in the United States

likely that the supply of objects which people are willing to buy has as yet reached the saturation level. But quite apart from that consideration, it seems likely that the per capita quantities of materials in use by industry must increase even though per capita production of consumer goods were to remain constant. The reasons for this probability become apparent when one examines the history of procurement and processing of raw materials.

When man first started to use metal tools he was able to find crystals of very high-grade copper ore on the surface of the ground.

As time went by, these easily accessible ores slowly disappeared, and man had to pursue the raw materials for his tools ever more deeply underground. Gradually even the underground deposits of high-grade ores became inadequate, and man had to develop a technology which permitted him to process ores of lower grade. Even so, by the turn of the present century we were still processing ores which contained 5 per cent copper. But mushrooming per capita demand, rapid growth of population, and the spread of industrialization combined to make enormous inroads into the available supplies of ore. The grade of available ore dropped rapidly. By 1953 we were mining ores that averaged 0.8 per cent, and even those containing as little copper as 0.6 per cent were being processed.

Thus, in order to obtain a given quantity of copper, about six times as much ore as was needed in 1900 must be processed today. And not only must a larger tonnage of ore be handled, but even larger quantities of useless rock or "overburden" must be removed in order to facilitate mining operations. As a result, the scale of operations on a low-grade ore body may be as much as fifty times as great as it was on a high-grade vein deposit.

Clearly it requires a great deal more technology, more equipment, more steel, and greater expenditure of energy to produce a pound of copper today than it required in 1900. And as we move to ores of still lower grade we will need even more technology, larger quantities of equipment, and greater expenditures of energy per pound of metal produced.

No matter where we look in the resources field, we find that this same situation prevails. The differences that exist are of degree rather than of kind. Our iron-ore deposits are striking evidence of the situation with which we must contend. Originally the United States was endowed with what appeared to be nearly limitless quantities of extremely high-grade iron ore. Indeed the Mesabi Range, where the greater part of these deposits was located, was a major factor in our rapid industrial development. These vast and magnificent deposits have, for many decades, been the principal source of raw material for our rapidly expanding steel industry.

But not so very many years ago we could glimpse the beginning of the end of the Mesabi's potential output of high-grade ore. The question then arose: Where does our steel industry go from here if it is to survive?

The fact that we have been running out of high-grade iron ore in the United States does not mean that we must eventually curtail steel production. But it does mean that we must take one or both of two possible courses of action. We can learn to process ores of lower grade, or we can import high-grade iron ore from outside the United States. Actually we are now investing heavily in both alternatives. We are building plants to upgrade the inferior and more difficult to handle iron ores known as "taconites" so that they can be used in our smelters. We are also investing heavily in developing sources of supply of high-grade iron ore in Labrador, in Brazil, in Venezuela, and in Liberia on the west coast of Africa. There is even some discussion of going as far afield as India for a part of our supply.

Clearly high-grade iron "ore" can be produced from taconites only at a cost—the cost of more technology, more equipment, and more energy per unit of output. But importing from distant points also involves high costs in ships, fuel, and manpower.

A similar situation exists in the aluminum industry. Domestic reserves of high-grade bauxite are inadequate to support our rapidly expanding domestic production, with the result that we import large quantities of the raw material. But here again the alternate path of processing low-grade domestic materials is open to us. There are vast amounts of aluminum-bearing clays in the United States which can be processed, and the technology of treating certain of them has been developed to the point at which aluminum can be economically extracted. A plant is now being planned for the Pacific Northwest which will produce alumina (aluminum oxide) from these clays. But just as in the case of iron produced from taconites, the costs in terms of equipment and energy are greater than the costs of processing bauxite.

Our need for water for industrial and agricultural purposes

provides still another example of increasing demands for equipment and energy. At one time ample supplies of water were available at very little cost. But the growth of industrial areas and the development of new agricultural regions eventually raised water requirements to a level at which they could not be easily met. Huge dams were built to impound large quantities of water. Lengthy

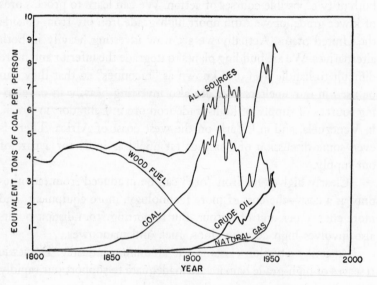

FIGURE 3

Energy Consumption per Capita in the United States, by Type of Fuel

aqueducts were constructed to transport the water over great distances. These developments resulted in the consumption of large quantities of concrete, steel, and energy.

This process is continuing. We must transport water over greater and greater distances. We must pump it from greater and greater depths. We must purify it from steadily increasing concentrations of pollutants. And we do these things only at the expense of adding more equipment to our industrial network and by expending ever larger quantities of energy.

Thus, no matter where we look in our modern industrial society, we find steadily increasing demands for materials even on a per-capita basis. And though even today's use of about 9 tons of steel for every person in the United States seems high by com-

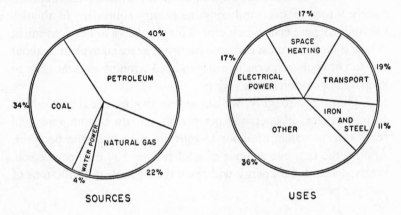

FIGURE 4

Sources and Uses of Energy in the United States (1953)

parison with the situation of fifty years ago, it will not be at all surprising if by the turn of the century this were increased to about 15 tons per person. Indeed it seems quite possible that perhaps 100 tons of steel may eventually be required to support a single human being in our society.

As quantities of materials in use increase, consumption of energy must increase also. Throughout our industrial history our per capita consumption of energy from fossil fuels and from water power has steadily increased. It can be seen from Figure 3 that our ancestors were prodigious but inefficient consumers of wood fuel. About the middle of the nineteenth century coal came into use in significant quantities, and per capita wood consumption dropped. Coal consumption rose rapidly until crude oil came into widespread use early in the twentieth century, followed shortly by natural gas. But except for the depression years, the total energy demands rose rather rapidly and reached the equivalent of about 8 metric tons of coal per person annually by 1950. In Figure 4 we can see the sources of our energy as of 1953, as well as the principal purposes for which it is used.

We have seen that we have in use in the United States approximately 9 tons of steel, and consume energy equivalent to about 8 tons of coal, per person, each year. This provides a rather convenient rule of thumb: we must consume energy at a rate equivalent to about one ton of coal each year in order to keep a ton of steel moving, to keep it in operation in our society.

Thus, very roughly, we can expect that by the time we have 15 tons of steel in operation per person, energy consumption will reach the equivalent of about 15 tons of coal per person per year. And by the time the amount of steel reaches 100 tons per person, yearly demands for energy will reach the equivalent of 100 tons of coal per person.

Five

TECHNICAL MANPOWER
IN AN INDUSTRIAL SOCIETY

As we have pointed out, man has gradually increased his demands for food, raw materials, and energy until he now consumes all of these things in tremendous quantities. How has he been able to meet these demands as they have arisen? What is the key to his continuing ability to increase his consumption at a rapidly growing rate? In order to understand how new and useful ideas have been translated into achievements it is necessary to examine the development of man's intellectual and technical skills.

From his earliest origins to the beginning of the Industrial Revolution, man's knowledge of the physical world was both limited and superficial. He was ignorant of the vast resources of coal, oil, and other raw materials hidden under the surface of the ground. He was ignorant of the laws of nature and the principles governing their operation. And he had no method by which he could identify these laws and principles. Some crafts he did possess—the skills for making tools, artifacts, and other objects—although these skills had developed only slowly. Up to the time of the Industrial Revolution only a small minority of the working population in any society was made up of skilled craftsmen. Since the skills to be learned were few, they were not taught in any formal manner but were handed down personally and individually from master to apprentice. Thus prescientific man possessed neither knowledge of the existence of the vast resources of the earth nor the skills necessary to extract these resources and put them to use. The raw materials which he did consume in order to maintain his harsh and meager existence were limited to such metals as gold, copper, and iron-materials readily available at the surface of the earth in highly concentrated or in pure form, and usable with little modification.

The working population of this prescientific society consisted mainly of farmers and to a lesser extent of tradesmen and unskilled urban laborers. Little education was necessary for the occupations of these men, and indeed formal education was limited to a few special groups, such as the nobility, members of religious orders, and some scholars. Nearly all the people of the world were illiterate.

But this all changed with the advent of the Industrial Revolution and the beginning of the scientific era. It was at this time that man first learned to combine coal, iron, and imagination to produce power and harness it to machines. Each coal-powered machine could do the work of many men and do so without strain or fatigue. It was inevitable that the demand for such machines should grow and that there should be an increasing need for workers with the knowledge and skill necessary to repair and maintain them, to build more of them, and to develop new ones. And so the skilled mechanic, the inventor, and the engineer came into being.

During this same time a new tool was being shaped, perhaps the most important man has ever developed. A few people here and there were making observations of physical phenomena, drawing conclusions from them, and making deductions which should be verifiable if the conclusions were valid ones. This method, which was first applied to the understanding of the physical world, has come to be known as the scientific method. And, as has become evident, it is of widespread use for gaining understanding of many facts concerning the physical and biological world, including man himself.

Man's knowledge of the world about him accumulated with

great rapidity after the beginning of the eighteenth century. As he applied this knowledge to improve his lot, he rapidly increased his consumption of energy and raw materials and his production of goods and services. Together with this increasing productivity, resulting from the application of more and more knowledge, a need developed for more skills and training on the part of the working population. The demand for skilled workers, for technicians, for engineers, and for scientists has gone ever upward with steadily growing rapidity. The increasing requirements for technical skill and knowledge have been paralleled by requirements for higher and higher levels of educational achievement for most segments of the working population. These trends have characterized the progress of the Industrial Revolution from its beginnings.

As time has passed, also, the need for unskilled laborers and farmers has progressively decreased—in the case of the unskilled laborer, because his jobs have been taken over by machines; in the case of the farmer, because his productivity has been increased by the development of agricultural technology and the mechanization of the farm. The increase in the demand for semiskilled and professional workers with specialized technical training can be clearly seen when one compares the working force in the United States at the turn of the twentieth century with that at present.

In 1900 there were 11 million farmers and farm workers in the United States. They made up 38 per cent of the entire working population, which then totaled 28 million. By 1950 the number of farmers and farm workers had declined to 7.5 million, representing only 13 per cent of the labor force, which had grown during the half-century to almost 60 million. Although our population doubled in this 50-year period, this smaller number of farmers is able to produce all our needed agricultural products and, in fact, to produce a surplus.

The upgrading of skills is clearly seen in two sectors of the United States labor force—the unskilled laborers and the professional groups. At the turn of the century, more than one out of every three workers were unskilled laborers. By 1950, however, only one in five workers remained unskilled. In the same period, the proportion of semiskilled workers in the total labor force increased from 13.4 per cent to 22.4 per cent.

Even more dramatic changes have taken place at the profes-

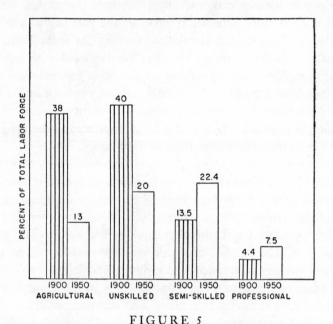

FIGURE 5

Changes in the Levels of Skills, United States Labor Force,
1900–1950

sional end of the manpower spectrum. In 1900 there were slightly more than 1 million professional and technical workers in the United States, making up not quite 4.5 per cent of the labor force. By 1950 this group had increased fivefold, now numbering 5 million, and constituting 7.5 per cent of the working force. It is perhaps even more significant that it continues to grow at a rapid pace.

When we look at different occupations within this professional group we see that the greatest increases have occurred among scientists, engineers, and technologists. During the 50-year period, engineers have increased tenfold, from approximately 40 thousand in 1900 to 400 thousand in 1950. Here, then, is a dramatic measure of the need for highly trained brainpower in the development and maintenance of a complex technical society.

The upward shift in the skills of the labor force has been accompanied by a fundamental change in the character of Western civilization. American social and industrial organization has become immensely complicated. It represents an intricately interwoven complex of mining, transportation, production, and communication facilities. Our economy is now entirely dependent upon these facilities and would quickly collapse if any one of them were to cease functioning properly. Each facility is similarly dependent upon the continued design and development of highly complicated equipment and machinery. Communication and control devices, transportation equipment, vast and highly coordinated production facilities are all dependent on the skill and knowledge of relatively few but essential scientists and engineers.

We can see this dependence most clearly when we contrast a highly developed urban-industrial society such as that of the United States with one that is predominantly rural-agricultural such as that of India. The United States has 1 technical school for every 4 million persons. India has 1 for every 25 million. The United States has 1 scientist or engineer for every 200 of its population; India has only 1 for every 30,000.

Today, for the first time in our history, we are running short of skilled technical brainpower. The broad-scale application of advanced technology has increased our consumption of technically trained persons to the point at which our available supply is no longer sufficient to meet our needs. The disparity between supply and demand has been emphasized by the officials of two hundred large companies which together employ well over half of all scientists and engineers in industrial research and development in the United States. When recently interviewed in a survey made by the United States Department of Labor for the National Science Foundation, the officials of more than half of these companies reported that shortages of technical manpower are either hindering present research activities or preventing desired expansions in their research and development programs.

We are immersed in a technical age which feeds upon technical brainpower. If we wish to produce more and more goods for more and more people from ores of lower and lower grade, then we must find the technical brainpower to develop the essential knowledge and to apply it with the necessary skill and diligence. Only in this way can a highly industrialized nation continue the development which is necessary to its maintenance.

Six

RATES OF INDUSTRIALIZATION

If the underdeveloped areas of the world were to industrialize to levels which approached, even remotely, those which exist today in the highly industrialized regions, demand for raw materials would become extremely high. About three-quarters of the present world population, or nearly 2 billion persons, are now living at extremely low levels of consumption. Suppose that by some miracle all these persons were to be brought suddenly up to the level of living now enjoyed by the people of the United States. In order to have accomplished this we would have had to extract from the earth about 18 billion tons of iron, 300 million tons of copper, an equal amount of lead, over 200 million tons of zinc, and about 30 million tons of tin, in addition to huge quantities of other metals and non-metals. These totals are well over one hundred times the present world annual rate of production. And although there is probably sufficient high-grade iron ore in the world to permit the extraction of 18 billion tons of metallic iron, the required quantities of copper, lead, zinc, and tin are considerably greater than could be removed from all measured, indicated, and inferred world reserves of ores of these metals.

In order to power this newly industrialized society, energy would have to be produced at a rate equivalent to the burning of about 16 billion tons of coal per year—an amount about ten times larger than the world's present coal production. There is probably enough extractable coal in the earth to permit such a level of production for quite a long time. But, as we shall see later, if any appreciable fraction of this energy consumption were to come from liquid petroleum, all potentially recoverable petroleum in the earth would probably be consumed in a very few years.

It is clear that no such miracle will happen overnight. Such a transformation takes time. Let us, then, inquire into the rates at which industrial growth might take place in the future.

We can obtain some idea of potential rates of growth by examining the rates at which industry has grown in the past, particularly in those areas of the world which have gone through the industrialization process relatively recently. Let us use as a measure the growth of the iron-and-steel industry, which is the backbone of modern industrial civilization. Per capita annual steel production, which ranges from about 9 pounds per person in India to about 1300 pounds per person in the United States, provides one of the best indicators of the industrial development of a country.

In the past such growth has characteristically followed the law of compound interest. Generally speaking, the greater the steel-production capacity of a nation has been, the greater has been the annual incremental growth, just as with a given amount of money in a savings account at a given interest rate, the annual income from interest increases each year, if none is withdrawn. We can speak of an annual growth rate in the same sense that we speak of an interest rate. And just as an investment at 6 per cent compound interest will double in value every twelve years, so a growth rate in the steel industry of 6 per cent per year corresponds to a doubling of production capacity every twelve years.

From about 1880 until the outbreak of World War I steel production in the United States doubled about every eight years. Following World War I the rate of increase lessened considerably, and of course during the great depression there was a sharp decrease in production. Since 1935 the doubling time for steel production has been about fourteen years.

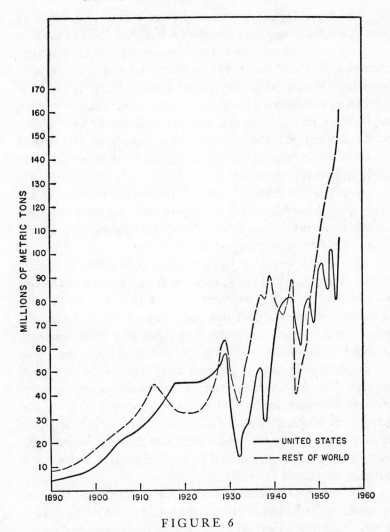

FIGURE 6

Steel Production in the United States and in the Rest of the
World

The beginnings of intensive industrialization in Japan took place at a considerably later date than in America. Prior to the Restoration of 1868, Japan possessed scattered small paper and porcelain industries, some coal mines, and some iron foundries. In the years following 1868 the Meiji government promoted, among many reforms, the development of strategic industries, including munitions, shipbuilding, mining, railways, and communications. Vaccination, posts and telegraphs, and steamships were introduced. Restrictions on Japanese travel abroad were removed, and Western advisers were freely and widely employed.

Aided by the knowledge that had been accumulated in the West, but hindered by severe shortages of raw materials and grave difficulties in the accumulation of capital, industrialization progressed steadily but not very rapidly.

World War I enabled Japan to make rapid strides in foreign trade and shipping, and this in turn greatly accelerated her rate of industrial development. Between 1913 and 1936 steel output rose thirty-fold, despite the fact that essentially all the basic raw materials, including iron ore, coke, and scrap, had to be imported. During this interval the doubling time averaged five years.

Between 1936 and the outbreak of World War II the rate of increase of steel production lessened, but Japan's output grew to the point where she produced about 80 per cent of Asia's total. The industry almost perished after Japan's defeat in World War II, but in the years that have followed the collapse capacity for steel production has been rebuilt, and in 1956 it actually exceeded that which existed at the start of the war.

The Industrial Revolution came to Russia late as compared with its advent in the United States and the nations of Western Europe. Russian industrialization was accelerated by an abundance of natural resources and by a flow of foreign capital. In the thirty-four-year interval from 1880 to the outbreak of World War I, Russian steel production increased about as rapidly as did production in the United States. During this period the doubling time was about seven years.

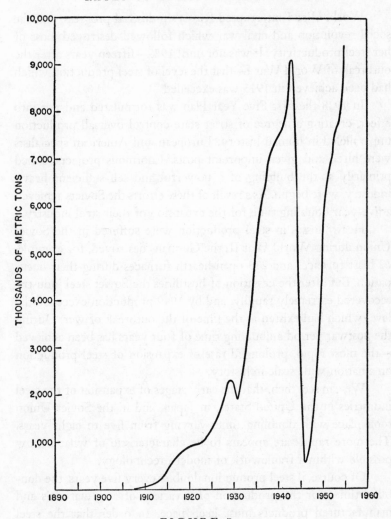

FIGURE 7

Steel Production in Japan

World War I interrupted Russia's industrial progress, and the social revolution and civil war which followed destroyed most of her steel productivity. It was not until 1929—fifteen years after the outbreak of World War I—that the level of steel production which had been achieved in 1913 was exceeded.

In 1928 the first Five Year Plan was formulated and put into effect, creating a degree of strict state control over all production unparalleled in human history. European and American specialists were hired and given important posts. Enormous projects, aimed primarily at the building of a powerful and self-sufficient heavy industry, were begun. As a result of these efforts the Soviets achieved a five-year doubling time for the expansion of their steel industry.

Heavy losses in steel production were suffered in the Soviet Union during World War II; the Germans destroyed, for example, 62 blast furnaces and 213 open-hearth furnaces during their occupation. But after the cessation of hostilities the Soviet steel industry recovered extremely rapidly, and by 1949 production exceeded the level which had existed at the time of the outbreak of war. During the postwar period a doubling time of four years has been achieved —the most rapid, prolonged rate of expansion of steel production on a nation-wide scale in history.

We can see, then, that the early stages of expansion of the steel industries in the United States, in Japan, and in the Soviet Union took place with doubling times varying from five to eight years. The more rapid rate appears to be characteristic of what is now possible within a framework of modern technology.

Of course, if steel production doubles every five years, the doubling times for the production of a variety of raw materials and manufactured products must keep pace. In order that the steel may be used, other metals such as copper, zinc, and aluminum must be produced; transportation facilities must be created; fuels must be mined.

Pig-iron production need not increase as rapidly as steel production, for the reason that steel plants feed in part upon recycled scrap. Thus in the United States between 1885 and 1915 pig-iron production doubled every twelve years while steel production doubled every seven years. In both the Soviet Union and Japan, however, the rate of increase of pig-iron production has very nearly equaled the rate of increase of steel production.

Let us now apply some of these considerations to the cases of specific underdeveloped and at present unindustrialized areas of the world. It is the declared intention of the leaders of both India and China, for example, to carry out programs of industrialization in their respective countries, aimed at creating something approaching Western levels of per capita production. If we assume favorable political, social, and economic circumstances, how rapidly may these goals be achieved? How rapidly can we expect the demand for raw materials in these areas to grow?

Steel production was started in India shortly after the turn of the century, and it has grown, although slowly. Twenty-six years were required for pig-iron production to double after 1924. At present this metal is being produced at the rate of 1.8 million tons per year, and steel at the rate of about 1.6 million tons annually. For many years India has ranked second to Japan in steel production in Asia.

In India's first and second five-year development plans heavy emphasis has been placed upon rapid expansion of the steel industry. The Indian government has contracted to purchase a steel plant from the Soviet Union, a second plant from a West German firm, and a third plant from the British. In addition, an American firm has contracted to extend the capacity of the largest existing installation. If all these plans are carried to completion, pig-iron production may reach 6 million tons annually by 1960–61, and production of finished steel, 4.5 million tons.

India is in the fortunate position of having at her disposal huge deposits of high-grade iron ore, favorably situated with respect to both coal and limestone. There is little doubt that she has ample iron ore to permit her to make the industrial transition and still have ore to spare. She is short of coal of metallurgical grade, but we know that there are technological means for circumventing this difficulty.

When we take these factors into consideration, it seems reasonable to suppose that, given a situation favorable from the social, political, and economic points of view, India should be able to achieve and maintain a rate of increase of her steel industry corresponding to a doubling of pig-iron production every ten years or so.

If we can assume that India is able to maintain a ten-year doubling time for a few decades following 1960, then pig-iron production would reach 15 million tons by 1975, and about 80 million tons by the year 2000. By that time a total of about 2 billion tons of pig iron would have been produced. Because of various losses of iron in use and in the steel cycle, the actual amount in use would be considerably less than this. And when we take into account further the large population increases which will undoubtedly accompany the process of industrialization, we realize that the per capita amount of steel in use in India in the year 2000 would correspond roughly to that which existed in Japan immediately prior to the outbreak of World War II.

As we know, it is necessary to produce, together with steel, a multiplicity of other metals and non-metals such as copper and zinc, coal and petroleum. If India's industry is to grow in a balanced manner, by the time her steel production reaches 15 million tons annually she will need to obtain in some way about 300,000 tons of copper, large quantities of lead and zinc, and about 30,000 tons of tin annually. By the time that steel production reaches 80 million tons annually, demands for these other materials would be increased still another fivefold.

It is probable that India does not have available deposits of ores of a number of needed substances in quantities which can even remotely fulfill these greatly expanded demands. This means that she will be forced to import them, and she will, as a result, become a competitor for a number of raw materials on the world market. In 1956 it appears, for example, that as time goes by she will become a heavy competitor for (to mention but a few shortages) copper and zinc, petroleum and sulphur. Substitute materials will be able to relieve some of the burden, but by no means all of it.

Similarly, although India has reserves of coal which are not negligible, that which is suitable for use in processing metals is limited. As a result she may be forced in the near future to shift to some process for producing pig iron which does not require coking coal. And her coal reserves themselves cannot last indefinitely. They are sufficient in size to get her well started along the path of industrialization, but it seems likely that, long before she achieves a per capita level of consumption approaching that of the West, she will be forced to shift over to some other source of energy, such as uranium.

All these factors will undoubtedly hinder her development. Unquestionably the task here is considerably greater than that which confronted the Soviet Union and Japan. Yet, as we shall see, when we examine the problem primarily from the technological point of view it is probably not incapable of solution. Barring social upheaval or war, a ten-year doubling time for Indian industrial expansion would appear to be a reasonable possibility.

It has been said that Asians do not really desire to emulate the West or to create anything approaching the per capita flow of goods which characterizes Western economy. Asians, it is said, would be content with a modest existence in which they are provided with sufficient food, shelter, and clothing, adequate schools and health services.

But the line of demarcation between a luxury and a necessity is a thin one. Even if we were to define a necessity as something whose sudden removal from our life would result in an increase in our death rate, many of the so-called luxuries of Western life would become classified as necessities. As luxuries appear and come into widespread use they are frequently transformed into necessities—even when a necessity is defined in this narrow way.

Thus, starting with the fountain pen and the wristwatch, which most Asians have seen and want, and which have become symbols, the list of Western "luxuries" which most Asians would buy, were they able to do so, is endless. But even the increase in industrialization necessary to enable Asians to reach the modest goal of adequate food, shelter, clothing, and health would be tremendous. In order to increase food supplies, fertilizers are needed. These require plants for making sulphuric acid and for fixing nitrogen. The plants require steel. Transportation facilities must be extended. Factories must be built for manufacturing antibiotics and vaccines. Schools and homes must be built. As the list grows, we find that, although the Asian would not need nine tons of steel in use per person, he would find it difficult to reach a minimum goal with less than one or two tons. And this represents a huge total requirement.

Thus, barring a world catastrophe, it seems likely that the industrialization process will continue at a rapid pace. But even with doubling times for industrial production which are as short as five years, many decades will be required before per capita levels of consumption throughout the world approach the levels now characteristic of the West. No matter how we look at the situation, the job that confronts the people of Asia is a prodigious one.

Seven

WORLD POPULATION

The population of the world has climbed with extraordinary rapidity during the course of the last century and has now reached a level of about 2.6 billion persons. The number of human beings inhabiting the earth is still increasing rapidly. But of even greater significance is the fact that the *rate of increase* is growing rapidly as well.

Between 1850 and 1900 the world society grew by about 0.7 per cent per year; this rate would produce a doubling of population every century. During the following half-century, between 1900 and 1950, the average annual rate of increase was 0.9 per cent, shortening the doubling time to about seventy-five years. If the projections of the United Nations are correct, the rate of increase will average about 1.3 per cent annually between 1950 and 1980 —indicating a doubling time of about fifty years. What are the reasons for this rapid population increase and for its rising rate?

The rate at which a population grows is determined by the difference between the birth rate and the death rate. In societies where sexual intercourse is freely practiced from an early age, where techniques of contraception and abortion are not generally used, and where cultural practices do not greatly inhibit conception, the birth rate may be between 45 and 50 births per 1000 persons per year. In many non-industrialized regions of the world it remains remarkably constant at about this average.

Throughout most of human history, however, death rates have

varied greatly from year to year and from generation to generation. Periods of famine have alternated with periods of abundance, periods of disease with periods of health. Infanticide has been practiced in some cultures. Wars, revolutions, and social upheavals have taken their toll. Natural catastrophes have swelled death rates.

Thus in some years there has been a net increase of population, while in other years there has been a net decrease. But throughout the greater part of human history deaths have, on the average, very nearly equaled births. With the average life expectancy at birth about 20 years (until comparatively recent times), the death rate has been in the neighborhood of 45 to 50 deaths per 1000 persons per year. This short life expectancy undoubtedly prevailed during the greater part of the time man led a food-gathering existence.

As various societies adopted agriculture their death rates probably dropped precipitously. Thus, as an increasing fraction of the world's population passed from a food-gathering to an agrarian existence, the population undoubtedly multiplied rapidly. But as towns and cities mushroomed and as the limit of food production, within the framework of the technology then available, was approached, pestilence, malnutrition, and famine again appeared, and once more the trend reversed itself and the number of people who died each year approached the number of people who were born. The average death rates eventually increased to the levels which had prevailed during the days of the earlier food-gathering cultures. We are reasonably certain, for example, that life expectancy at birth in certain of the great ancient urban centers such as Rome was only about twenty-five years.

With the emergence of the scientific-technological-industrial society, lowered death rates appeared once again. The new and decreasing death rates resulted from a multiplicity of causes, all of which were rooted in the new power which man was gaining over his environment. New and greatly extended transportation systems permitted man to carry food from areas of abundance to areas where famine threatened. New power permitted man to extend his agricultural land rapidly. New knowledge permitted him to obtain higher crop yields per acre. Later, as knowledge concerning public health was accumulated, death rates fell even more precipitously.

The major decreases in death rates have taken place in the younger age groups throughout the Industrial Revolution. Infant mortality rates have shown the greatest reductions, followed by those among persons under thirty years of age. Although the lowering of death rates for persons over forty has been substantial, it is small when compared with the reductions among the younger age groups. This lengthened life expectancy for very young people has meant that more girls have lived to and through the childbearing years. And this in turn has accelerated the rate of population growth.

The constant lowering of the death rate in England and Wales is a good example of the general trend. About 32 per 1000 in the middle of the eighteenth century, it had dropped to about 22 by 1850, and is now about 11 per 1000. For nearly a century following 1750 the birth rate remained at a level of about 37 per 1000, with the result that during this period the rate of increase of population grew to nearly 16 per 1000 or about 1.6 per cent per year. Had the birth rate remained high during the following century, the rate of increase would have grown further and would today be over 2.5 per cent per year. But instead, as the population grew and as culture patterns changed, the birth rate started to drop. This drop began about 1850, and in less than a century the birth rate fell from 37 to about 12 per 1000. The fall resulted in part from changed culture patterns, such as postponement of marriage, and in part from the adoption of techniques of contraception. As the birth rate fell the rate of population increase stopped rising and fell to very low levels.

Throughout the greater part of the Western world the process of industrialization has been accompanied by very nearly this same pattern of population growth. The early period of industrialization has been characterized in each case by high birth rates, falling death rates, and rapidly expanding population. This has been followed by a period in which birth rates as well as death rates have fallen, and in which the maximum rate of increase has been passed. At present in most Western nations, death rates are low and birth rates fluctuate.

In the United States, as in other Western countries, both birth rates and death rates fell steadily until the outbreak of World War II. During this period the rate of population increase fell to about 0.8 per cent per year. But both during and following the war the

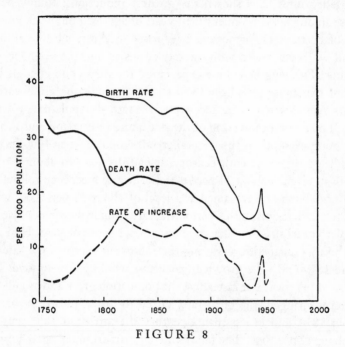

FIGURE 8

Vital Statistics for England and Wales (1740–1955)

birth rate increased markedly, with the result that the rate of population growth increased rapidly as well, as happened in practically all the industrialized nations of the West. In Western Europe, after the postwar baby boom, the birth rate again approached the low levels which characterized the immediate prewar period. But in the United States, for reasons which are only poorly understood, it has not only remained high, it has increased further as time has gone on.

Today, with a birth rate of over 25 per 1000 and a death rate of only 9 per 1000, the United States has one of the highest rates of natural population increase in the world, about 1.6 per cent annually. When we add to this immigration, which corresponds to an annual increment of about 0.2 per cent, we have a total rate of population increase of about 1.8 per cent per annum—considerably higher than the rates of increase in Italy, Japan, or India. The Bureau of the Census estimates that if our birth rate does not drop soon our population may reach 190 million by 1965. And it seems likely that we will cross the 200-million mark by 1970.

The rapidity with which birth rates can change makes the task of projecting the population of the United States more than a few years into the future a hazardous one. Nevertheless it is doubtful that our population will be much less than 225 million in 1975, and it may well be over 300 million by the end of the century.

In most of the unindustrialized areas of the world birth rates remain high and approach the biological maximum. But in many of those areas, largely as the result of the application of certain features of Western technology, such as mechanical transportation and public health, death rates have fallen during the last fifty years. In India, for example, population was apparently at one time effectively limited in large part by recurrent famines. But with the construction of extensive transportation and irrigation systems, famine was virtually eliminated and population steadily increased.

But all too often outright starvation was replaced as a major cause of death by an increased incidence of a variety of diseases—malaria, cholera, plague, smallpox, tuberculosis, yaws, syphilis, and bilharzia, to mention a few. The susceptibilities of individuals to these diseases were accentuated by chronic and widespread malnutrition. Nevertheless, the net result of the spread of mechanical transport, irrigation, and medical services, coupled with improved government organization, has been to reduce death rates slowly but rather steadily. Kingsley Davis, one of our outstanding demographers, has shown, for example, that between 1925 and 1944 the crude death rates in eighteen underdeveloped countries declined on the average by 6.3 per cent every 5 years (see Notes).

Thus a new phenomenon has appeared in the modern world

—declining mortality and expanding population in the absence of significant economic improvement. Indeed the evidence suggests rather strongly that in most underdeveloped countries the lot of the average individual has worsened appreciably during the last half-century. People have become more poorly fed. There are fewer available goods per person. And practically every attempt to improve the situation has been nullified by the relentless pressure of continued population growth.

The situation that prevailed in the underdeveloped regions of the world prior to the close of World War II was disquieting. But that which has developed during the last decade in the areas which have inadequate food supplies is disturbing in the extreme. For example, Kingsley Davis has shown that the average mortality in eighteen underdeveloped countries during the period 1945–49 was 15 per cent less than it had been during the previous five-year period. In the following half-decade there has been a 20-per-cent decline in mortality. These greatly accelerated reductions in mortality were not associated with any appreciable economic development within the areas themselves, yet the reductions were greater than those which in the past have occurred during the periods of most rapid economic improvement of the nations now industrialized.

We do not have to look far to find the reasons for the amazingly rapid decline in mortality in the underdeveloped areas. It is now possible to treat on a mass basis many of the diseases which are widespread in underdeveloped countries, and we have found that the control can be achieved at low cost. Insecticides such as DDT, vaccines such as BCG, and antibiotics such as penicillin are some of the developments which have made control possible on a mass basis.

The widespread spraying of the island of Ceylon with DDT resulted in a decrease of mortality by 34 per cent in one year alone. This decrease reflected an enormous reduction in the incidence of malaria in addition to a reduction in deaths from a variety of other insect-borne diseases. The use of DDT in Greece has likewise greatly reduced the incidence of malaria, and at extremely low cost. It is now believed that yaws can be cured on a mass basis at a cost of only

$1.00 per person treated. By the use of penicillin, endemic syphilis has been eliminated as a public-health problem in large areas.

In practically all these areas the birth rates have not decreased appreciably. The prevailing high birth rates coupled with drastically lowered death rates have resulted in enormously accelerated rates of population growth. The population of Costa Rica is growing at a rate of 3.7 per cent per year, and that of Formosa at 3.5 per cent per year. The rates in many other areas are nearly as large: Mexico, 2.9 per cent; Ceylon, 2.8 per cent; Puerto Rico, 2.8 per cent—all compared with a world average of a little more than 1 per cent.

Such rapid rates of population growth can, in the long run, be maintained only if the production of food can keep pace with population growth. As we shall see later, it seems doubtful that this can be achieved for any prolonged span of time. In any event such rapid increases in numbers of human beings, were they to continue, would eventually completely cover the earth with people. At the rate which now obtains in Formosa, for example, in but 450 years there would be one person for every square foot of land area in the world.

The United Nations in 1954 estimated that in 1980 the population of the world will be between 3.3 and 4.0 billion and gave 3.6 billion as the probable figure. It is dangerous to attempt to forecast the probability much beyond 1980 on the basis of present trends. In a transition period such as that which we are now experiencing, where not only death rates but birth rates can change quickly, extrapolations into the future can soon be shown to be erroneous. If we were to assume, for example, that the increase in population during the next century would average 1 per cent per year, we would foresee a world of nearly 7 billion persons by the middle of the next century, or, if we based our calculation on a rate of growth of 1.5 per cent, the number would be about 12 billion persons.

In spite of the difficulties it is interesting to project the future on the basis of reasonable assumptions concerning rates of industrialization and, related to them, rates at which both death control and birth control are adopted by various cultures. If we assume, for example, that rates of population growth in the West will fall to very

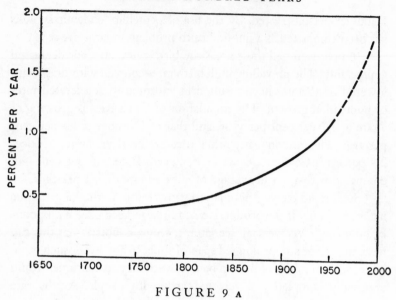

FIGURE 9 A

Annual Rates of Increase of World Population

low levels by 1975, that rates of growth in Japan, Eastern Europe, and Oceania will fall to low levels by the turn of the century, that Africa, South-Central Asia, and most of Latin America will pass through the industrial transition in 75 years, and that a full century will be required for most of China and the Near East, then we arrive at a world population of nearly 5 billion by the year 2000, and nearly 7 billion by 2050.

These estimates assume a rather rapid spread of acceptance of birth-control techniques. Without such acceptance, the increase may be much greater than this. On the other hand, no matter how optimistic we are, it is difficult to visualize a set of circumstances not involving widespread catastrophe, which can result in a leveling off of world population at much less than 7 billion persons.

Thus, in our forecasts concerning the future, we must examine the problem of feeding this number of persons adequately. And we

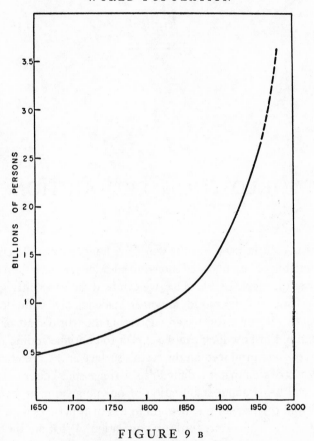

FIGURE 9 B

Growth of World Population since 1650

will use this figure for the purpose of computing resource needs for a highly industrialized society on a long-range, self-sustaining basis. But we should remember, when we refer to a long-range, stabilized world population of 7 billion persons, that this is a minimum. The earth may well be called upon to provide for a substantially higher population than this minimum estimate.

Eight

WORLD FOOD PRODUCTION

More than half the people of the world are hungry today. Each day, also, something like a hundred thousand additional mouths join those already at the world's table. That we can feed the constantly growing population of the world, however inadequately, is due to the fact that by diligent effort we are increasing the world's rate of food production. For how long can we expect to continue adding to the amount of food produced on the earth's surface at the present rate?

We have seen that it is difficult to envisage social circumstances which will bring about stabilization of our population at less than several-fold the present number and in less than perhaps a hundred years. Can our agriculture feed this population? What are the limits on the amount of food that can be produced upon the surface of our earth each year? These are the questions which we must now consider.

During the entire history of mankind, human numbers have been very largely limited by the amount of food available. Since the advent of agriculture about seven thousand years ago, the domestication of plants suitable for man's food has made possible a very great increase in human population and a considerable stabilization of man's way of life, though periodic crop failures and the resultant famines continued to limit the rate of human increase up to about the seventeenth century. From this time on, as we have seen, human numbers have increased at an ever more rapid rate. This has been made possible by our increasing ability to carry food about from regions of plenty to regions of deficit and thus to even out the catastrophic effects of local famine. During these last three centuries

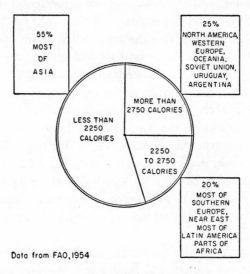

Data from FAO, 1954

FIGURE 10

Proportions of Population Living at High, Intermediate, and Low Caloric Intakes per Capita

human beings have covered more and more of the earth's area, until today the regions suitable for our present type of agriculture are largely occupied. And finally, the technical and agricultural revolutions of the past century have increased our knowledge of how to grow food plants and domestic animals and have permitted us to use our land more effectively.

Despite our increased agricultural skill and effort, however, more than one-half of the population of the world receives today a barely minimal food supply and continuously lives on the verge of starvation, as is indicated in Figure 10. Another quarter of the world's population is undernourished. Only the populations of

North America, parts of Europe, the Soviet Union, Oceania, and a small part of South America are not hungry. Indeed, the high dietary standard enjoyed by those of us who live in the United States is shared only by the peoples of Canada, Australia, New Zealand, Argentina, and Uruguay—who together constitute about 9 per cent of the world population.

Nor does it appear that the food deficit of the world will be ameliorated in the near future without widespread improvements in education and techniques. Indeed, the amount of food produced in the world as a whole increased by but 10 to 15 per cent during the forty years preceding the beginning of the Second World War, while the population of the world increased during the same period by about 30 per cent. The Second World War markedly decreased food supplies over much of the earth's surface, and the prewar level was not regained until 1952, by which time there were, of course, more people to feed. As a long-term trend, then, a vast number of the world's people have been not only hungry but growing steadily hungrier.

Let us consider first the present production of food, the characteristics of our agricultural framework. We may next examine the factors which limit production of food, and analyze the rates at which we might expect food production to increase during the years to come. Finally, we may examine the limits upon the production of food by our conventional agriculture in the world as a whole.

Man's food is derived directly or indirectly from plants, which possess the power to transform the carbon dioxide of the atmosphere into the variety and complexity of chemical substances which are necessary for the maintenance of man. A portion of our plant material we eat directly—the cereal grains, and many vegetables, for example. A further portion is converted into meat, milk, eggs, by being processed through domestic animals. Nonetheless, in principle, "all flesh is grass."

The human individual, to live an energetic, healthy life, needs to eat enough food each day to supply him with about 3000 calories. To obtain these, he must consume each day the equivalent of about

1.8 pounds of plant material containing about 0.7 pounds of carbon. This carbon is contained in a great variety of the chemical substances which make up plants.

The human being consumes about 260 pounds of carbon per year. Let us now compare, as is done in Table I, the amount of food

TABLE I. *Annual World Production of Plant Material, Its Distribution, and Its Fate*

	AVAILABLE CARBON (BILLIONS OF TONS PER YEAR)	POPULATION THAT COULD THEORETICALLY BE ADEQUATELY SUPPORTED (BILLIONS)	RATIO TO 1955 POPULATION
Created by photosynthesis			
World	150	1160	460:1
Land	16	120	49:1
Cultivated land	4	30	12:1
Fate of carbon from cultivated land			
Plants consumed by animals (½), 3% of which is converted into food for human beings	0.06		
Crop plants (½), 20% of which becomes food for human beings	0.4	3.5	1.4:1
Actual plant material available, after 35% losses due to insects, other pests, disease	0.3	2.3	less than 1:1

[55]

required by each human being with the total amount produced by plants each year. The photosynthetic transformation of the carbon which is part of the carbon dioxide of the atmosphere to the carbon of plant material takes place on a vast scale. Each year over the surface of the earth as a whole, some 150 billion tons of carbon are converted from carbon dioxide to plant material. This plant substance, if it were consumed in its entirety by human beings and completely digested by them, would suffice to support about five hundred times the current world population. Unfortunately, most of the photosynthesis of the earth's surface goes on in the waters of the oceans and is used but little by our human population. Even so, if the plant material produced upon the land surface alone were consumed and digested completely by human beings, it would suffice to feed about fifty times the present population.

Because of their dietary habits, however, human beings confine themselves almost exclusively to cultivated plants or to animals which feed upon cultivated plants, and these constitute less than one-fourth of the annual photosynthetic increment of the land surface. The cultivated produce would, however, if eaten in its entirety by human beings, still suffice to feed more than ten times our current world population.

The harvest of our cultivated lands does not suffice to supply our current population with an adequate diet because it is frittered away by a series of major leaks in our systems for food-plant utilization. Thus, approximately half of the produce of our cultivated acres is fed to domestic animals. The animal eats only a part of the plant, and what he does eat is returned to us as animal products suitable for the human diet—meat, milk, eggs, and so on, with a caloric yield of perhaps 10 per cent. We feed the animal 100 calories worth of potential food for human beings; he spends 90 calories walking around and keeping warm and returns to us only 10 calories as food.

A second major loss in utilization of the produce of our cultivated acres arises from the fact that the human being does not eat all the plant. Thus with wheat, for example, we eat the seed and reject the stems, leaves, and roots. On the average, perhaps 20 per cent of the plant is consumed as food by man. And finally, our produce is not eaten by man and his domestic animals alone, but is shared with other creatures. The pests, the insects, fungi, rabbits, kangaroos, and so on, consume one-third or more of the food which otherwise would be available for the maintenance of human beings.

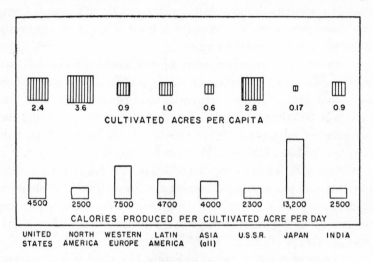

FIGURE 11

Agricultural Production and Yields

And as our yearly harvest is subjected to these losses and diversions, barely enough remains to feed the current world population.

The world actually provides a great excess of potential food material—over 150 tons per person per year, as compared to the 0.3 ton which each human being requires. We would have sufficient food if it were not for the losses and inefficient use of it discussed in the previous paragraphs.

The distribution of our food-producing land is also vitally pertinent to the world food situation. There are today about 2.4 billion cultivated acres in the world, or very nearly 1 cultivated acre for every living human being. The people are distributed, however, quite inequitably over these acres, as is shown in Figure 11.

At one extreme, the United States possesses more than 2 cultivated acres per capita. In North America as a whole, which includes Canada, with its vast farm lands and relatively small population, each person is served by 3.6 acres. At the other extreme, Japan possesses less than 0.2 of a cultivated acre for each inhabitant. In Asia as a whole each individual is supported by just over 0.5 of a cultivated acre, while the Western European has at his disposal a little less than 1 cultivated acre.

Further, the cultivated acres of the world are farmed with widely differing effectiveness. In the United States we produce to-day about 4500 calories of potential food per acre per day. This yield is greater than that of Asia, which averages about 4000 calories per acre per day, although productivity levels are higher in East Asia than in Southeast Asia. Western Europe, with its more intensive agriculture, is producing about 7000 to 8000 calories of potential food per acre per day. Japan, which has the world's most intensive agriculture, produces over 13,000 calories of potential food per acre per day—over 3.5 times as much as the world average of 3800 calories per acre per day.

The productivities shown in Figure 11 are calculated in terms of potential food for human beings—that is, production of material without regard to whether it is fed to and eaten by human beings directly or fed to animals for the production of animal products. There are, of course, very great differences in practices of food utilization in different areas of the world—chiefly in the varying degrees to which animal products are included in the human diet. These are summarized in Figure 12.

The American feeds most of his plant material to his domestic animals. This is true, for example, of our two major cereal crops, corn and oats, of which only a negligible amount is eaten in its original form by human beings. Almost all of them are fed to animals and converted to animal food products. The American consumes, in fact, about one-third of his diet calories in the form of meat, milk, eggs, and so on. The Asian, on the other hand, eats most of his plant material directly, consuming less than 5 per cent of his calories in the form of animal products. The Western European steers a middle course, feeding a little more than half the produce of his cultivated acres to domestic animals, and consuming about 20 per cent of his diet calories as animal products. These food habits are related

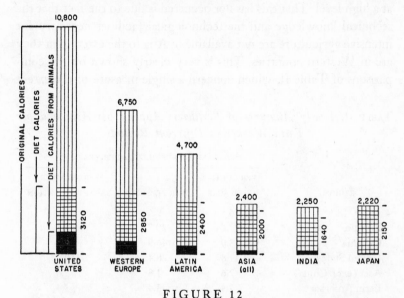

FIGURE 12

Daily per Capita Production and Consumption of Potential
Food Calories

directly to the number of available acres per person. Only those regions which have a surplus of land—a high ratio of acres to people—can afford the luxury of processing their food through the animal.

Differences in agricultural productivity in different regions do not appear to be primarily attributable to inherent differences in soil fertility or climate. They reflect rather the technological level of the culture and the density of its population. Although we in the United States have at our disposal all the agricultural technology known to the Japanese, we do not cultivate our land as intensively as do they, for we have so much land per capita that this intensity is not yet necessary, and it is economically more profitable to use more acres less intensively than fewer acres more intensively.

In Asia, outside of Japan, people are hungry, and there is, in principle, every reason for productivity per acre to be maintained at a high level. That this has not occurred is due to the fact that the technical knowledge and the technological facilities necessary for intensive agriculture are not available in Asia to the extent that they are in Western countries. This is very clearly shown by the comparisons of Table II, which concern a single measure of the extent

TABLE II. *Yearly Amounts of Fertilizers Applied per Acre and per Farm Worker in Different Regions*

| | KILOGRAMS OF FERTILIZERS PER YEAR 1953–54 | | |
| | PER CULTI- | | PER MEMBER |
REGION	VATED ACRE	PER PERSON	FARM POPULATION
Japan	56.5	9.6	19.2
Europe	22.6	20.7	63.2
Oceania	13.0	46.9	142
United States	11.8	28.4	150
Asia (excl. China)	2.6	1.8	2.6
Latin America	2.4	3.4	5.4
Africa	0.4	0.9	1.1
India	0.3	0.2	0.3

to which technology is applied to agriculture, namely the use of fertilizers.

Europeans apply over twice as much fertilizer per acre per year as do Americans. The rate of application in Japan is again twice that of Western Europe. In India, on the other hand, fertilizer is used but little since it is not available in quantity nor is the Indian farmer well informed concerning fertilizer application. Similar comments may be made about plant improvement by plant breeding or the control of pests by chemical pesticides, both of which are practiced intensively in the Western world but are not available to the under-developed areas.

It is primarily the application of science to the fertilization and irrigation of plants, to the genetics of plant improvement, and to the killing of pests, that has brought about the increased yields per acre in Western countries over the yields characteristic of primitive agriculture. Farm mechanization has also contributed to some extent in increasing yields by making possible more favorable adaptation of farming operations to weather conditions.

But we must not overestimate the importance of mechanization so far as yields per acre are concerned. Mechanization has had its biggest impact in increasing productivity per farm worker, in reducing the number of man-hours needed per unit of agricultural output, and in liberating people from agriculture for productive activity in industry. It is in fact still quite apparent that in technologically developed countries there is a close relation between intensity of agriculture as measured by productivity per acre and the proportion of the labor force used in agriculture. Thus, Japan, which has the world's highest productivity per acre, uses about half its labor force to produce these high yields. In Western Europe roughly a quarter to a third of the population is engaged in agriculture, while in the United States only 9 per cent of the labor force works on the land. Intensive agriculture still requires the application of intense human effort (see Notes).

The comparisons of Figure 11 indicate, then, that it should be possible to produce more food on the area of the earth's surface now under cultivation, and that this might be accomplished merely by spreading to the underdeveloped areas the technology and facilities which are available and which support intensive food production in the developed countries. It should be possible to double, or more than double, the average productivity of areas of the world already under tillage by merely raising the productivity of the land to that characteristic of Western Europe today. All we need to do, in principle, is to practice all over the world the techniques now used in developed countries—the techniques of fertilizer production and application, of plant improvement by plant breeding, and the control of pests.

Let us therefore ask how rapidly we might expect agricultural productivity to increase as the result of the diffusion of present agricultural technology. A good way to approach this matter is to examine the time course of food production increase in countries which have already undergone agricultural and industrial revolu-

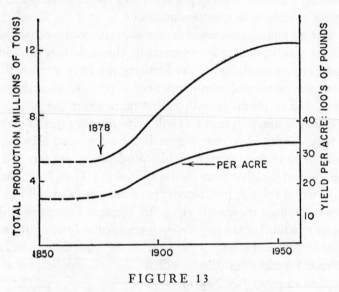

FIGURE 13

Rice Production and Rice Yield per Acre in Japan (from Japanese Ministry of Agriculture and Forestry)

tions. In Japan, for example, the technological revolutions commenced in the middle of the nineteenth century. For a long period preceding 1870 the population of Japan remained relatively stable, as did also rice production and food production generally. Precise figures for cultivated acreage and productivity per acre are available for the period from 1878 to the present. The curves of Figure 13 concern the production of rice, a crop which supplies the Japanese with over half their diet calories. Beginning in the 1870s, the total rice crop of Japan rose slowly but regularly, more than doubling over a period of fifty to sixty years, an increase effected primarily by increased yield per acre. This was achieved by more widespread use of fertilizer and by the application of genetics to the production of higher-yielding varieties.

The increase in Japanese agricultural productivity in the last quarter of the nineteenth century and the first quarter of the twentieth century was closely paralleled by a similar increase in Western Europe. In both cases food production increased by roughly 2 per cent per year, to double over a period of fifty to sixty years. Agricultural growth is therefore slow as compared to industrial growth. We have already seen that during this same period the steel production of Japan doubled approximately every five years.

Agricultural productivity, as we have seen, increases from an initial low level and tends to approach an upper limit. Japanese productivity, for example, has changed but little since 1935, despite intensive technological effort. Industrial productivity will someday approach an upper limit—a limit which we will reach as we begin to stabilize our mining operations upon the leanest of ores, the rocks of the earth's crust and the waters of the seas. But we are still very far from approaching the limits of our industrial productivity, even on the basis of present technology. We are not so far from the limits of our agricultural productivity and it is possible, as in Japan, to attain this limit within a few generations. The records of the past century have shown that industrial productivity tends to rise in geometric progression, but agricultural productivity does not.

In the past, then, increases in agricultural productivity have taken place at the rate of roughly 2 per cent per year, both in the Asian and in the European framework. Is it possible that more rapid increases might be achieved in the future, now that we know more about agricultural technology and, possibly, more about how to spread it? The answer to this question is that we do know how to increase food production now, and to speed, but not greatly, the rate of its increase. In the United States, for example, with all our biological and agricultural knowledge and a superb farm-advisory service, agricultural productivity has been increasing by about 2 per cent per year for the past twenty years, as shown in Figure 14. Our increase in food production is thus nicely keeping pace with our rate of population increase. In the United States, of course, we have an adequately fed population and no urgent reason for more

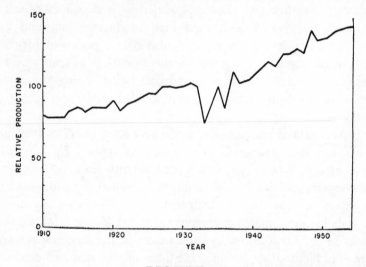

FIGURE 14

Annual Food Production in United States since 1910
(1935–39 = 100%)

rapid increases in food production than are indicated by increases in numbers of people. Let us therefore consider an undernourished country.

A well-conceived program of the Rockefeller Foundation has helped to bring about an increase in food production in Mexico of about 80 per cent in less than 20 years—a rate of increase of nearly 4 per cent per annum. Per capita supplies of food have increased appreciably during this period, even though population has increased during the period by about 3 per cent per year.

The remarkable increase of food production in Mexico has been brought about by increases in the acreage of cultivated land, by greatly increased irrigation programs, and by agricultural education and research efforts. Mexico has received a great deal of technical assistance from the United States in the execution of these developments. This achievement represents perhaps what we may expect as an upper limit on rate of expansion of agricultural production today, at least in the absence of new social techniques.

The rates of increase in food production in Asian countries today are much less than that achieved by Mexico and in fact barely exceed the rates of population increase. This is true even in countries such as India in which vigorous governmental efforts have been and are being made to improve food supply. Approximately one-fifth of the funds devoted to India's first five-year development plan were allocated to agriculture. Irrigation projects have been established, fertilizer plants constructed, educational services extended. This effort has resulted in an increase in total food supply of approximately 15 per cent, or 3 per cent per year. India's people are, however, still less well fed than they were before World War II, since India's food production, before the five-year plan, remained constant for a dozen years, while her population grew rapidly.

Agricultural productivity may then be expected to increase with sufficient skilled effort. A rate of 2 per cent per year can certainly be achieved, and this might be raised to as much as 4 per cent per year with exceptional effort. We have seen that the population of the underdeveloped areas is increasing at rates of from 1.3 per cent to over 3 per cent and that there is every reason to anticipate further rises in this rate. It would seem therefore that the best we can hope for by the spread of our present technology to the underdeveloped areas is an increase in food supply at a rate only slightly greater than the rate of increase in numbers of people. Any slacking off in the diligence with which we spread our technology to the underdeveloped areas will result, as it did during the Second World War, in food deficits, hunger, and misery.

The curve of Figure 13 shows that we may expect food production, by our conventional agriculture, to increase to some maximum level and then approach a ceiling above which it is apparently difficult to rise. The low productivity per acre of most of the world's farm land justifies our anticipating large increases as we spread our current technology. But in the long run food production by conventional agriculture, as it is brought to a high state of efficiency, will approach a ceiling.

How many people can we feed on the earth's surface as we approach this limit? Before we can discuss this matter, we must consider the limits upon the number of acres used for agriculture on the earth as a whole. The lands now in use for the production of crops are of certain specific types which are both fertile and relatively stable under present agricultural practices. The brown chernozem soils of the temperate regions, and the red laterites of the less rainy tropics are the most fertile and the most easily cultivated areas. These soils are completely occupied by human beings and their agriculture at the present time.

In order to gain more acres for our agriculture it will be necessary to expand the cultivated area into lands which are more difficult to use—the podzols of the wet cold regions and the laterites of the more rainy tropics. There are technical difficulties in the utilization of these lands, especially those of the wet warm regions. These soils are difficult and expensive to fertilize and to maintain in a state of good tilth because of the high leaching and erosion rates.

It is probable that these difficulties can ultimately be overcome. It has been estimated that approximately 1 billion new acres of cultivated land could become available to agriculture through the subjugation of parts of the warm and cold wet regions of the earth. The introduction of this vast new acreage into cultivation would have its greatest effect in North and South America, where it would increase the cultivated acreage by 50 to 60 per cent. It would have its least effect in land-deficient Asia, where it would increase cultivated acreage by less than 30 per cent. Let us suppose, however, that the productivity of both the presently cultivated area and of the newly subjugated land is raised to that characteristic of Europe today. This would be a level of productivity almost twice the present world average and would, as we have seen, require 30 to 50 years to achieve. To bring about this increase in food production would be a major financial task, requiring the investment of perhaps 500 billion dollars. Funds would be required to establish throughout the world intensive farm-advisory service, such as we have in the United States; to establish educational facilities for the training of farmer and farm-adviser alike; and to provide scientific research facilities for the solution of agricultural problems. It would require major capital investment in plant facilities to manufacture the fertilizers and other chemical materials required. Something like twenty times the present world-wide production of phosphate would be required.

But in any case, these tasks once accomplished, how many people would our agriculture support? Table III indicates that agriculture prosecuted on this intensive basis would suffice to feed 4 to 5 billion people on a calorically adequate diet. This assumes that the peoples of Asia would continue to content themselves with

TABLE III. *World Populations That May Be Supported at Different Levels of Land Productivity and of Human Diets (Assuming all potentially arable land to be in use)*

PRODUCTIVITY OF LAND	TYPE OF HUMAN DIET	POPULATION SUPPORTABLE (BILLIONS)
Present European level	Present European, 3000 calories per day	3.7
Present European level	Present Asiatic in Asia, European elsewhere, each 3000 calories per day	4.8
Present Japanese level in Asia, European elsewhere	Present Asiatic in Asia, European elsewhere, each 3000 calories per day	6.5
Present Japanese level in Asia, European elsewhere	Present Asiatic in Asia, European elsewhere, each 2500 calories per day	7.7

a diet containing but a small proportion of animal products. It assumes furthermore that the people of the rest of the world's area content themselves with a diet providing only about 20 per cent of their calories in the form of animal products—a diet healthful and adequate, although not to us gastronomically exciting.

If the peoples of Asia were to content themselves with a diet somewhat lower in calories, our intensive conventional agriculture should certainly suffice to feed a total of perhaps 5 billion people. And, as we have seen, this is the population which we must expect for our world within 50 years. Our conclusion must be, then, that application of our present agricultural technology can in principle take care of our growing population's food needs for the next 50 years.

What will happen as world productivity per acre approaches the levels characteristic of Western Europe? Can we hope for further increases? An answer to this question can be hazarded on the basis of the productivity of present-day Japan. Japan, by intensive farming, maximum application of scientific knowledge, and lavish use of human labor, achieves a level of productivity almost twice that of Western Europe today. If we are able in the long run to achieve this level of productivity on one-third of the earth's agricultural acres and a level of productivity of present-day Western Europe on the other two-thirds, it will be theoretically possible for us to support between 7 and 8 billion people at a reasonable standard of living. It will certainly be a very long time before these high levels of productivity can be attained, perhaps 75 to 100 years. But it will also be quite a long time before 8 billion people daily present themselves to be fed. And when they do, from the technological point of view, we should be able to supply them.

Our conclusion is, then, that increases in food supply are attainable by wider application of present technology. Agricultural productivity can be increased by the use of more irrigation, more fertilizer, more insecticides; by the application of more plant-improvement techniques; and by practicing more intensive agriculture along the lines practiced in Japan. The rate at which such increase can be achieved is between 2 and 4 per cent per year and should thus suffice to take care of our increasing world population. By the time, perhaps in 75 to 100 years, that the average productivity of our arable acres has been raised to the levels that we now know to be possible, world population may have become stabilized. Conventional agriculture will apparently suffice to feed 7 to 8 billion people, although only at standards of living lower than those of the best-fed peoples today.

Nine

NEW KNOWLEDGE AND NEW FOOD

As is pointed out in the preceding section, it will be possible to double or quadruple the world's production of food by stepping up our agriculture in the ways now used in Western Europe and in Japan, and by using more of the earth's potentially arable area. These are increases in food supply which may be achieved merely by actually doing things we already know how to do. True, to spread this technology will be a long, hard task, since it must diffuse to so many people, but theoretically it can be done.

And meanwhile new technological developments may increase the rate of growth of our food supplies or raise the maximum amount of food which can ultimately be produced, by the introduction of new methods of management of crops and of human diets.

A most effective method of increasing the amount of food available to people would be to decrease that fed to animals. Animal protein forms an important part of the human diet today, particularly, as we have shown, in the Western countries. We consume animal protein not only because it tastes good to us but also because it provides a plentiful supply of the amino acids essential to human nutrition, in the most favorable proportions. Yet these same amino acids are present in the protein of plants, from which the animal product has derived them, and with proper preparation can be effectively used. As we have seen already, the animal is a relatively inefficient converter of plant material to food for human beings. Table IV summarizes data on the yields of protein obtainable per acre of cultivated land by different systems of management. The production of protein by conversion of plant substance to beef, which supplies about one-half of the world's meat, has an efficiency of only 5 to 10 per cent, both in terms of food calories and in terms of protein. The production of milk protein is considerably more efficient than is the production of beef. Both of these procedures are, however, much less efficient than it would be to use our crop area for the production of soybeans, which produce seeds rich in protein, and eat the soybeans ourselves. And the plant which produces seeds rich in protein is, again, less efficient as a protein producer than is a plant such as alfalfa, which is rich in protein in all its vegetative structure (see Notes).

TABLE IV. *Production of Protein per Acre by Different Methods of Land Management*
(*All values for cultivated crops on arable land*)

METHOD OF LAND MANAGEMENT	METHOD OF RECOVERING PROTEIN	EDIBLE PROTEIN (POUNDS, PER ACRE PER YEAR)
Planted to forage, grain, fed to steers	as beef	43
Planted to forage, silage, fed to cows	as milk	77
Planted to soybeans	as soybeans	450
Planted to alfalfa, U. S. average crop	as extracted protein	600
Planted to alfalfa, Western U. S. irrigated	as extracted protein	1500

Alfalfa is, of course, grown to supply protein for animal diets, and there is no reason in principle why it cannot be used to supply protein directly in the human diet. If we are to use plant protein on a large scale as food for people, however, it will be necessary to devise methods by which the plant may be ground and the protein extracted. We will also have to find ways of fabricating the protein thus extracted into materials resembling meat, milk, eggs, and so forth. But these are merely technological problems and are certainly soluble. This modification of our food technology would permit us to supplement human diets with the needed amino acids at a fraction of the cost in acres that characterizes our present system.

A second modification of our agriculture which could provide an important increase in the world's food supply is the replacement of crops which are less efficient in food production by crops which are more efficient. This raises the question of the efficiencies of different crop plants. Wheat yields less food per acre than do rice, potatoes, or sugar beets, but this is in part because the land sown to wheat is often less favored by rain or temperature than are the lands chosen for the other crops. Similarly, yields are often low in the underdeveloped areas because of limited supplies of fertilizer.

Let us, then, compare the efficiencies of crop plants as producers of food when each crop is grown under conditions as nearly ideal as possible. Such a comparison is made in Table V. It is clear that the cereals compare unfavorably with potatoes or sugar beets, since high-yielding crops of the latter produce up to twice as many

TABLE V. *Efficiency of Various Crops in Production of Food in Varied Regions*

REGION	CROP	FOOD PRODUCED (MILLIONS OF CALORIES PER ACRE PER YEAR)
United Kingdom, moderately intensive farming	cereals (wheat)	2.9
	potatoes	6.7
	sugar beets	7.3
Northern Europe (Denmark, Holland), intensive farming	wheat	4.5
	potatoes	8.0
	sugar beets	13.0
Japan, intensive farming	rice	6.5

or more edible calories per acre per year as do the cereals. This is due to two principal factors. For one thing, the potato or sugar-beet crop takes longer to develop than does the cereal. Leaves that are exposed longer to the sun's energy have more opportunity to gather and store that energy. And in the second place, 50 or 60 per cent of the potato or sugar-beet plant is edible and digestible by man, as contrasted to 30 per cent or so of the cereal.

To look at it in another way, the energy which is stored in plant material is energy the plant has captured from the sun's rays. Plants as we know them appear to be very similar in the efficiency with which they store solar energy in chemical form. Given favorable temperature, plenty of water, and abundant fertilizer, our crop plants uniformly capture about 2 per cent of the incident energy, and this efficiency is actually achieved in our best and most intensive agriculture today (see Notes).

High yields of food material per acre are attainable if we use a crop which remains active in the field for a long time. Thus the tropical sugar cane, which captures the sun's energy the year round, readily produces twice as much sugar per acre as does the sugar beet, which grows for but five months or so. And in addition, the chemical equivalent of 2 per cent of the sun's incident energy must be divided among the varied portions of the plant. The grain is a smaller portion of the cereal than is the sugar of a sugar beet. These considerations are clear enough and provide us with a clear-cut goal in plant improvement. We want a plant which grows over a long season and of which as high a proportion as possible is edible. The commercial sugar beet is in fact a product of genetic improvement by which the original low-sugar plant has been bred for high sugar content and high per-acre yields. We know how to breed crop plants high in other constituents, such as fat and protein. It is not at all impossible that we might be able to alter our sugar-producing plants by genetic means to cause them to accumulate fat, protein, or other dietary necessities in higher yield. Thus, we might breed a meat beet or a fat plant.

There is still another approach to the problem presented by

the fact that only a relatively small portion of the cultivated plant is edible to the human being. We can convert the inedible residues to food. Such residues are abundant. In the United States, for example, in which the human being yearly eats about 0.37 ton of food, we produce each year about 1.75 tons per capita of the inedible residues of corn and wheat—stalks, stems, corn cobs, et cetera.

The technology of the conversion of these woody materials to material digestible by man is well worked out. It is possible to treat the woody plant material with hot acid and produce a molasses-like syrup of roughly 50 per cent of the weight of the original material. The present estimated cost of molasses from this source is roughly ten times that of molasses from sugar beet or sugar cane. It is further possible to convert the molasses by yeast fermentation to a protein-rich material. The yeast obtainable from the molasses in 50-per-cent yield is also potential food for man. If the need for food in the world were great enough we could theoretically convert the bulk of our woody residues to sugar or protein by this method, a measure which by itself would increase our food supply by perhaps 50 to 100 per cent. The food increment would be costly, since it would require the expenditure of a great deal of energy and investment in much new technology, but it could be done, should it become necessary.

The step which appears, however, to be most practical for the ultimate augmentation of our world's food supply has to do with the management of water. Water availability is today a major limiting factor in crop production and in determining crop areas. There are in addition vast areas of steppe and desert which would be suitable for agriculture if water were available.

At the present time about 11 per cent of the world's cultivated acres are supplied with water by conventional irrigation schemes. This amount is rapidly increasing, particularly in Asia and Latin America. It has been estimated that if the waters of the rivers of the world are appropriately conserved and distributed it should ultimately be possible to irrigate 14 per cent of the world's cultivated acres at current prices of water and of farm products. This amount could undoubtedly be increased still further, perhaps to as high as 20 per cent of the world's cultivated acres, by the building of expensive conventional irrigation projects. There is nonetheless just not enough water in the streams to irrigate any substantially greater portion of the earth's surface than this, by conventional methods.

We cannot hope, therefore, to water the steppes and deserts, which together constitute over twice as large an area as the land now under cultivation, by conventional irrigation projects. If we are to irrigate this area we must acquire water from other sources, and this means in the long run the reclamation of sea water. What are the economic prospects for the reclamation of sea water and for the irrigation of the deserts of the earth in this way?

It is now economical to carry on agriculture in the United States in regions in which irrigation water from conventional projects costs as much as $10 per acre-foot and in which from 2 to 5 feet are applied per acre per year. It is proposed to intensify this practice within the next 20 years with irrigation water that costs up to $40 per acre-foot. Supplementary irrigation in the southeastern United States, the application of relatively small amounts of water to enable plants to survive through drought periods, is already being carried out with water which costs as much as $75 per acre-foot.

The cost of reclamation of ocean water has been investigated by various groups. These forecasts agree in suggesting a probable cost for fresh water from the sea of from $100 to $200 per acre-foot. To this we must add the cost of building canals and pipelines to carry and distribute the water. And so, if we are to irrigate the arid areas of the earth with reclaimed sea water, we will do so at great expense. To supply irrigation water alone will cost more per acre per year than the average value at present prices of the crop produced on such an acre.

But as our world becomes more populous and as the need to obtain more food becomes more pressing, we have available to us this straightforward means of extending an otherwise conventional agriculture to a very large area indeed. It would probably be possible to double or quadruple the world's ultimate food production by supplemental irrigation of the less favored portions of our present crop land and by extending irrigation to the areas which are now arid.

It has been shown that although nine-tenths of the photosynthesis of the earth's surface occurs in the oceans, still, only a small portion of the resulting material finds its way into the human diet. We harvest sea produce primarily in the form of fish, which contribute a negligible fraction of the diet calories that today support the world's human population. We know too that we cannot greatly extend the fish harvest without depletion of the ocean's fish populations. Why is it that the ocean's potential contribution of fish is so small, even though the ocean's yearly crop of algae is so large? The answer to this question seems to be that it takes a lot of algae to make even a little bit of fish. It has been estimated that about 100,000 pounds of algae will produce only 1 pound of codfish. The alga is first consumed by some microscopic animal, which retains about 10 per cent of the calories. This small animal is next eaten by a larger one with another energy recovery of 10 per cent, and so on and on. The food chain from alga to fish involves three, four, or five steps. Only a food contribution of from 0.001 to 0.1 per cent of the original plant material is eventually available as fish for the diet of human beings. By and large, then, the fish is an inefficient converter of plant to human food. If we wish to use the ocean efficiently as a source of food, we must apparently make unconventional approaches to the harvesting of plant material from it. We could of course strain the algae from ocean water directly by some mechanical means, but we would have a lot of straining to do, since 1 cubic meter of sea water contains on the average about 1 cubic centimeter of plant material. We might, however, contemplate the possibility of using the ocean as we do grazing land. We might domesticate an ocean-going vegetarian beast—a sea pig.

The cultivation of algae as a food crop has been widely discussed in recent years. In principle it should be possible to cover an area with large tanks, fill these tanks with an appropriate nutrient solution, inoculate them with a suitable type of alga, and harvest the algae periodically. If the tanks were covered with transparent plastic or glass, the carbon-dioxide content of the atmosphere could be enriched, thus leading to a production of larger crops for a given area than would be obtainable in the open. At the same time, however, such closed tanks must be cooled in some way, since they act as heat traps when the sun shines upon them. Conventional crop plants as well as algae respond to increased carbon-dioxide concentrations by increased yields. The advantage of algae lies principally in the fact that it is technically rather simple to supply them with extra carbon dioxide.

The investment in preparation of land for the culture of algae is, however, ten to one hundred times greater than that for conventional agriculture. Yield of plant material per unit area of surface exposed to sunlight and under equivalent carbon-dioxide concentration is the same for algae and for conventional crop plants. And when the algae have been finally grown and harvested, we have merely a nasty little green vegetable, the consumption of which presents the same sorts of technological and psychological problems as are associated with the utilization of, for example, alfalfa as food for man. It seems logical to conclude that expansion of our food supplies by the more familiar agricultural techniques will precede expansion of our food supplies by the cultivation of algae.

The chemical synthesis of food would also appear to be an exceedingly remote possibility, at least so far as provision of general diet calories is concerned. The human being requires in his nutrition chemical compounds which are complex and exceedingly various. Although we do know how to use simple compounds as the starting materials for the chemical synthesis of the sugars, fats, amino acids, and vitamins required in the human diet, it is still a complicated chemical job.

Perhaps the most elaborate large-scale efforts to produce human-diet calories by synthetic means was undertaken by the German government during the Second World War. In order to cope with a severe shortage of edible fats, factories were made to synthesize fats, starting with the hydrogenation of coal. The process was extended with major effort until it supplied about two thousand tons of fat per year, about one-thousandth of the amount yearly consumed in Germany.

Chemical synthesis of food is a big job. We should bear in mind, too, that it cannot be based permanently on the use of petro-chemicals (chemicals obtained from coal and petroleum) as starting materials but must ultimately be based on the reduction of carbon dioxide, as is agriculture itself.

Although the chemical synthesis of bulk dietary calories appears to be impractical for the foreseeable future, that of dietary supplements is a practical matter even today. It is possible to supply a human being with his required rations of vitamins, all synthetically produced, at a cost of between $0.25 and $1.00 per year. The vitamins, although complex and expensive to manufacture, are required by human beings only in minute amounts.

It is also possible to supplement diets with synthetically produced amino acids, although this is still of questionable practicality from an economic standpoint. Populations in underdeveloped areas who live primarily on cereal diets sometimes suffer from amino-acid deficiencies, probably through lack of the amino acids methionine, lysine, and tryptophane. A year's supply of these three amino acids, synthetically produced, costs today approximately $40 per person, so that it is hardly feasible economically for most of the world's population to supplement diets with them.

It may well be, however, that in the future we can enrich our diets with an increasing variety of synthetically produced materials, devoting our agriculture to the business of supplying the bulk of the calories we need.

We have dealt in this chapter with some of the ways in which major changes in food production may be brought about in the course of the next century. We may anticipate other less dramatic advances too—continued improvements in pesticides, for example—which permit us to reduce the losses of our crops to insects, fungi, weeds, and other pests and diseases. We already have other basic information which may constitute the basis for agricultural advances in the foreseeable future. There has been, for example, a great deal of discussion in the past as to whether crop yields can be maintained at a high level or whether our agricultural procedures will gradually result in depletion of soil fertility, especially by destroying the particulate structure, the tilth, of soil. A properly structured friable soil is important if high yields are to be obtained. Since our ordinary agricultural practices tend to destroy soil structure, it is customary to practice crop rotation, in order to alternate structure-depleting crops with soil-building plants. We now know, however, that it is possible to improve the physical structure, the granulation, of soil, by the addition of appropriate synthetic materials, certain polyelectrolytes such as Krilium. The use of such synthetic soil-structure-building materials is at present economically unfeasible, but the problem of cost can probably be solved if the need for the materials becomes sufficiently important. Control of soil structure by this method could result in significant increases in food-plant yield by permitting monocrop practices—by relieving the farmer of the obligation to return his land periodically to crops which are good soil conditioners but calorically poor.

We are just beginning to have some knowledge of the chemical mechanisms by which plants sense and adjust themselves to the temperature in which they grow. Thus it has been found that in some cases crop plants grown in a climate unsuitably hot or cold can be caused to grow more normally by the application of appropriate chemicals. A knowledge of the chemical mechanisms which limit growth rates in unfavorable climates might enable us to match plant and environment artificially at a more nearly optimum level and over a wider climatic range. This would increase crop yields in part by permitting cultivation in the temperate zone through a greater portion of the year.

One of the important limiting factors in crop production, especially in the underdeveloped areas, is the availability in appropriate form of nitrogen-containing fertilizer. The leguminous plants, however—the peas, beans, et cetera—unlike our other crop species, do not need nitrogen fertilization. They possess nodules on their roots which are inhabited by bacteria capable of reducing the molecular nitrogen of the atmosphere to the level of ammonia, a form of nitrogen suitable for use by the plant. Leguminous plants are for this reason frequently used in crop rotations to supply nitrogen to the soil and thus to support the subsequent growth of calorically more valuable food crops. We can envisage the possibility that geneticists and plant physiologists, once they have gained adequate knowledge of the factors responsible for the nodulation of leguminous plants, might then be able to transmit this character to other crops, such as the cereals, making them also independent of nitrogen fertilization.

The scientific study of agricultural problems is recent, just over a hundred years old, and there is much left to discover about plants and animals. We can expect with some confidence that important new principles will be discovered and important agricultural applications made in the future, principles and applications which may make it possible to grow more food on less land and with less human effort. But even if such new principles are not discovered, we can still, as we have seen, increase the amount of food available for human beings merely by the further expansion of principles which we now have at our disposal.

One such step is already being taken—namely, the replacement of less efficient by more efficient crops of which a larger proportion is edible. It will be possible, too, to increase the efficiency of production of protein and of fat by technological advances which will permit us to obtain these materials directly from the plant rather than secondarily through animal products with the attendant caloric loss which this involves. And, finally, if the need becomes so great that it overrides the high costs involved, supplementation of our present irrigation water by water reclaimed from the ocean would seem to promise very great possibilities for the expansion of our cultivated area and of our food resources in the years to come. The principal limitation upon the amount of food which we can produce is the amount of technology and the amount of energy which we are able and willing to devote to the matter.

Ten

PATTERNS OF
AGRICULTURAL CHANGE

As food supplies have increased through the centuries, they have been matched by increasing human numbers. The race between people and food is much clearer and much sharper today than at any previous time in history because modern public-health measures have raised rates of population growth to higher levels than ever before. The food supply of the world is nonetheless increasing, and we can expect it to continue to increase. The technology which is at our disposal today should make it possible to double the world's total food production, and this at a rate which is sufficient, if we apply ourselves, to keep pace with the rate of population growth for the next fifty years.

This is an optimistic conclusion and one that people like to hear. But the mere fact that it is theoretically possible to increase food production should not blind us to the magnitude of the task. It is immense. Agriculture involves more of the people of the world than any other productive activity. To change its procedures we must change attitudes and beliefs of a majority of the people of underdeveloped regions. And attitudes and beliefs change slowly, over generations rather than over years. In spite of the accumulation of knowledge over a period of a hundred years, there are still many people in Western societies who hold that to replace manure with mineral fertilizer is dangerous if not indeed poisonous for plants. Agricultural changes require, therefore, influencing great numbers of people about matters on which they are slow and difficult to change. The social and psychological problems of increasing food production are therefore large ones.

The spread of agricultural technology not only involves education of a vast number of people but requires vast tonnages of materials which must be made, transported, and applied to land, and still vaster tonnages of produce which must be transported, stored, and distributed. And these matters too will require enormous outlays of capital and human effort, and a complicated technology.

To achieve the increases in food production which we know to be possible appears to require deliberate effort on the part of society —of government. In the absence of such organized effort, the people of whole nations can and have rapidly become hungrier, even in recent years.

The increases in the world's food supply which we can make today are those most readily achievable—those attainable by use of better crop plants and animals and by the use of more and better fertilizer. The increases in food supply which we will bring about in another half-century will be more difficult ones, most costly in energy and requiring advances in technology.

Each successive increment in food supply may be expected to be a more costly one. Our question is really not so much one of the food potential of the world, as one of the effort which must be expended in order to supply the food needed to support our world population at any given time in the future. What kind of agriculture will be required to support the human population at the level at which it finally becomes stabilized? This question has already been discussed in world terms, implying that food surpluses from one region may be moved to regions of food deficit. In actual fact, however, only a small and decreasing portion of the world's food, less than 7 per cent at present, moves in international trade. In general, each nation, each geographic region, largely feeds itself.

Let us look, therefore, more particularly at some specific areas of the earth's surface and discuss the differences of their food problems.

The United States is now in a period of rapid increase in food yields per acre. This trend is one which can continue for the next twenty-five to fifty years, on the basis of knowledge we now have. We should therefore be able to support our increasing population at the present high standard of living for some time to come. But even should we fall behind in the rate of increase of our agricultural productivity, we still have an enormous food resource to call upon in our high per capita production of original calories. We produce for each person in the United States today over 10,000 calories of potential food daily, although the human being requires for his maintenance but 3000 calories. The corn, oats, and other grains fed to livestock could, if diverted to the feeding of human beings, support a very large number of people indeed. Thus if we were today to drop our daily intake of animal products to the level of the Western European diet (20 per cent of our diet calories), we could support over 250 million people on a calorically adequate diet. This reserve constitutes a vast cushion upon which we can draw for food in times of stress or of unduly rapid increase in our American population. It would appear that if, in the very long-range future, our population should stabilize itself at 300 to 400 million people, we should be able to feed them all by conventional agriculture and on a healthful diet.

Europe as a whole is a region of moderately high food productivity today. The productivity of the poorer regions of Southeastern Europe can be raised by more thorough application of present technology, but the productivity of the intensively food-producing countries of Northern Europe is already at a high level and can increase but slowly and only as new technology is made available. Western Europe is and has been for fifty years a net importer of food from countries which now have less to export as their own populations rise. Fortunately, the population of Europe is growing only slowly. It appears probable, however, that unless stabilization is closely approached during the next fifty years, Europe will have to resort to greater importations, lowered living standards, and possibly to some methods of agriculture not now in use.

The greatest food-production problems of the world today are those which exist in Asia, and particularly in Southeast Asia. This region is at present the most crowded and the most poorly fed portion of our planet. But its agricultural problems can be eased by spreading and using the technological knowledge we now have. Even though this is a difficult job, it is being accomplished by the establishment of new educational and research institutions, the education of millions of people, and the replacement of old agricultural patterns by new ones. The rate of growth of food production in a considerable part of Asia is keeping up with the rate of increase of population and can apparently continue to do so for a very long time to come. The limits of food production by conventional agriculture are, however, such as to permit the feeding of the Asian population only at a very low standard of living by the end of the next fifty years or even the next century. In order to improve the standard of living of the Asian peoples it may well be necessary to resort to measures of unconventional agriculture.

The agricultural problems of the underdeveloped areas of Latin America, Africa, and Oceania differ from those of Asia in that population densities are not so high, and more potentially arable land, even though it presents difficult problems, remains to be developed. In each of these areas it would seem to be quite feasible to increase food production by conventional agriculture at a rate sufficient to provide adequate diets for the populations which will appear by the time stabilization has occurred.

The problems of agriculture and of the expansion of agricultural production are not only technological but also economic and social. We are attempting today to grow more food in the underdeveloped areas by means which take capital investment—by irrigation projects, manufacture and distribution of fertilizer, education, and so on. This makes food more expensive. And the food consumer, in order to buy this food, must therefore have an increase in income. Consumption of food in areas of low per capita income is extremely sensitive to slight changes in food prices as well as to slight changes in income of the consumer. The result has been that in underdeveloped areas with strong agricultural-development programs food supplies have tended to accumulate even though people remain hungry. Consumption as well as production of food must apparently go hand in hand with increases in industrialization and increases in per capita income. Expansion of income, of tangible reward in the form of increasing ability to purchase the objects available in the culture, is necessary both for the farmer who is to grow more food and for the consumer who is to use more food.

With the spread of industrialization the problems of the agricultural producer do not end. We have seen that industrial productivity tends to increase according to the laws of compound interest. As industrialization progresses, an ever larger portion of the total population is drawn from agriculture to the factory, and in the factory the productivity of the industrial worker increases steadily. The total output of our industrial network and the income of the industrial worker thus increase at an ever more rapid rate. The output of the farm network rises much more slowly, geared as it is to the number of people to be fed, and as a consequence agriculture becomes an ever smaller part of the total economy. The income of the farmer in relation to that of the industrial worker would therefore rapidly drop were it not balanced by other factors. We have managed this situation in the United States by rapid increases in the productivity of the agricultural producer, attended by decreases in the absolute numbers. Even so, per capita income of the farmer has tended to lag behind until it is now but 40 per cent of the income of the industrial worker. Between 1850 and 1955 the proportion of farm workers in the total labor force dropped from 64 per cent to 9 per cent. While the number of industrial workers has risen at an ever increasing rate, the number of farm workers has actually decreased—a trend which is still continuing.

At what level will the number of farmers become stabilized? How many farmers do we need to feed an industrialized society such as that of the United States? We cannot yet answer this question, although it seems fairly clear that the number required

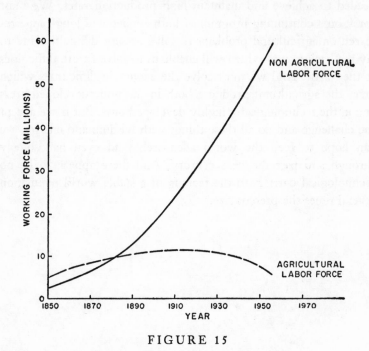

FIGURE 15

Changes in United States Labor Force, 1850–1953

may well be several million. But in any case the consumption of food in an industrial civilization does not increase as rapidly as does the consumption of the produce of expanding industry. It seems inescapable, therefore, that in an industrial society the maintenance of per capita farm income, when it can no longer be achieved by continuing reductions in numbers of farm workers, will have to be accomplished by other economic measures.

There are, then, many problems which must be solved and there is much work to be done to achieve the increasing production of food demanded by our growing population. We must spread the science and technology of farming. We must build, over the world, facilities for agricultural education, for the manufacture of the industrial products such as fertilizers, tractors, and pesticides, needed to achieve and maintain high production rates. We must carry on a continuing program of both applied and long-range research on agricultural problems to solve present difficulties and to lay the background which will enable us to solve future difficulties as they arise. And we must solve the economic difficulties which beset the agricultural producer both in the underdeveloped areas and in the technologically highly developed ones. But if we accept the challenge and do all these things with wisdom and energy, we can hope to feed the world adequately and even handsomely through and past the next century. And there appear to be no technological barriers to the feeding of a stable world population several times the present size.

Eleven

WHAT IS A RESOURCE?

We have seen that if the standards of living of the people of the world are to be brought up to levels that will enable them to lead reasonably healthy lives, industrialization must spread throughout the world. This transition is necessary if we are to increase appreciably the amount of food which is produced in the world each year and if people are to be provided with a minimum of certain of the necessities of modern life such as schools, hospitals, medicines, adequate shelter and clothing.

We have also seen that as industrialization spreads throughout the world the demands for raw materials will become enormous, and indeed will dwarf existing demands. As demands increase and as the world's high-grade resources are consumed, it will become necessary for us to process materials of lower grade, making our demand for raw materials increase still further as a result of the fact that more equipment, more energy, and more technology will be required for the processing.

What, if any, are the limits to the grades of ores which can be processed? Is it possible for the trend toward lower- and lower-grade materials to be continued indefinitely? Or is there some limit of concentration below which processing will become impossible? Since the beginning of the present century, as we have seen, the average grade of copper ore in use has dropped to one-sixth the concentration formerly processed—that is, to about 0.8 per cent copper. Can we look toward the possibility of processing ores which contain as little as 0.1 per cent, or perhaps as little as 0.01 per cent copper?

When we examine this problem from the technological point of view, we see that fundamentally there is no lower limit to the grade of an ore which can be processed. This was illustrated dramatically by the isolation of the new element plutonium during World War II. This substance, produced in nuclear reactors, was isolated in an Oak Ridge pilot plant from uranium metal which contained plutonium in concentrations measurable only in parts per million (1 part per million = 0.0001 per cent). The uranium metal, which could be looked upon as a plutonium "ore," was put through a sequence of elaborate chemical processes. The plutonium was concentrated, and it was eventually isolated in pure form and in high chemical yield. The plutonium was, of course, very expensive. But the important principle is that there were no technological barriers to prevent its eventual isolation.

Similarly, if at some future time the average concentration of copper in copper ore were to drop to 0.01 per cent, and if there were still an acute need for copper, there would be little question but that the metal could be extracted in high yield. To make this possible, two criteria must, however, be fulfilled. First, a satisfactory process must be developed—which means that scientists and engineers must work on the problem in the laboratory and in the pilot plant and conceive, develop, and test various methods for achieving the desired result. Second, energy must be available for the processing—for the mining and transport of vast quantities of ore, for the manufacture of the huge quantities of equipment which must be used in the processing and as a driving force in the process itself. As we shall see, if we are given adequate supplies of energy almost any material in the earth's crust can be looked upon as a potential resource. On the other hand, if we are given only extremely limited reserves of energy our resource potential will likewise be extremely limited.

As is pointed out later, the ultimate resources of energy which are available to man are enormous—and indeed are sufficient to power a highly industrialized world for literally millions of years. This means that, given adequate brainpower, there is little doubt that the trend which has led us to process ores of steadily decreasing grade can continue until we reach the point where we are processing the very rocks of which the earth's crust is made.

Ordinary igneous rocks contain most of the elements necessary for the perpetuation of a highly industrialized society, and in proportions which are not unreasonable from the point of view of industrial needs. One hundred tons of average igneous rock contain, for example, about 8 tons of aluminum, 5 tons of iron, 180 pounds of manganese, 40 pounds of nickel, 20 pounds of copper, and 4 pounds of lead. Many of the elements which are not found in sufficient quantity in igneous rocks, such as chlorine, bromine, and iodine, can be found in the oceans. Other elements, such as nitrogen and oxygen, are readily available in the atmosphere. Still others can be found in the practically inexhaustible supplies of limestone (a source of carbon), gypsum (a source of sulphur), and phosphate rock (a source of phosphorus). Given the brainpower and the energy, the people of the world could, if need be, support themselves entirely with the leanest of ores, the waters of the oceans, the rocks of the earth's crust, and the very air around them.

When we look into the future we can foresee many steps which will take place as we progress toward the processing of these ordinary substances. Clearly, before man processes average rock on a large scale he will process richer-than-average rock. He will isolate an increasing fraction of his iron from intermediate-grade ores such as taconites. As supplies of coking coal dwindle, iron ores will be reduced with hydrogen, produced initially from coal of poorer quality, but in the long run produced from sea water. Increasing quantities of aluminum will be produced from clays. Sulphuric acid will be made from pyrites, then from gypsum. Copper, tin, lead, nickel, and germanium will be isolated from a variety of intermediate- and low-grade deposits.

Changes from one type of technology to another and from one type of raw material to another will take place irregularly in the various regions of the world. Clays will be processed in one region while bauxite is being processed in another. The use of taconites will become widespread in some regions while other regions are still able to obtain their iron from high-grade ores. Some regions will reclaim sea water on a large scale while others will enjoy adequate supplies of fresh water from rivers and lakes. But gradually the leveling effects of resource depletion will result in a general convergence of techniques and of raw materials—and mineral resources as we now know them will cease to play a major role in world economy and politics.

It should be noted that recycled metal scrap is becoming an increasingly important source of raw materials in the world. Theoretically, if the world were eventually to accumulate a sufficiently large quantity of each of the metals, and were to find it feasible to recycle metals with 100-per-cent efficiency, it would no longer be necessary to produce metals from ores, save enough to replace that which is irretrievably lost through rust, attrition, sunken ships, et cetera. But in actual practice, of course, losses cannot ever be entirely eliminated. The proportion of a metal which is lost irrecoverably will depend upon the amount of effort and energy which is required to prevent the loss, or to recover it, as compared to the amount of effort and energy which is required to produce new metal from ore. In principle, losses of metals can be greatly decreased, but only with substantial expenditures of money and of energy per unit of metal output. We can expect that as time passes and as we extract metals from lower-grade ores, there will be an increasing economic incentive to prevent the loss of metals in use, to increase the efficiency of scrap recovery, and to decrease losses in cycling.

As time goes by there will likewise be increased incentive to recover other substances which are essential to industrial civilization. As we move toward the reclamation of sea water we will move toward the reclamation of sewage and industrial wastes. Already the treated sewage of the city of Baltimore is providing a convenient source of water for a large steel plant, and the sewage of Milwaukee is providing an excellent source of organic fertilizer. As the years pass we can expect enormous improvements in the reclamation of wastes of all kinds.

But it must be stressed that materials obtained by recovery from waste or by preventing the loss in the first place are not without cost. In the long run, efforts aimed at decreasing losses and at increasing recovery result in greater consumption of coal and petroleum. The best we can do is to balance the value of the substance which is lost against the value of the energy and effort which would be required to prevent the loss. Thus it appears likely that even were world population and the per capita quantities of metals in use stabilized, there would be a continuing and substantial demand for new metal, determined in effect by the energy expenditure required to obtain new metal relative to the energy expenditure required to prevent the loss of old.

Another important aspect of the raw-materials situation during the next century concerns the use of substitute materials. Starting with the "substitution," many centuries ago, of iron for bronze, there has been a continuous flow of new materials into our lives, ranging from new metals to new foods to new materials of construction. Undoubtedly during the decades and centuries ahead many additional materials will be developed which can either substitute for others currently in use or make possible the fabrication of machines and structures which previously could not have been built.

In recent years we have seen aluminum used to a limited extent in place of steel. In the years ahead we will undoubtedly see other substances such as fiberglass-plastic laminates replacing steel in certain types of structures. Already we have seen a variety of synthetic fibers replacing silk, wool, and cotton, and in the years to come we will see most of nature's fiber products replaced by the products of the chemist.

Nevertheless there are uses for which it does not appear to be possible to substitute materials which are easily produced and relatively inexpensive for materials which are expensive and rare. It is difficult, for example, to visualize a substitute for germanium in transistors or for uranium or thorium in large-scale nuclear reactors. It is equally difficult to visualize a replacement for tungsten, tantalum, or molybdenum in the vacuum tube.

A number of substitutes are, however, clearly possible, although adoption of the substitutes might necessitate rather drastic changes in the designs of certain of our machines and gadgets. Copper, which is particularly useful because of its high electrical and thermal conductivities, provides an interesting example in this respect. Although aluminum does not conduct electricity as well as copper, we see steel-reinforced aluminum cable replacing copper in long-distance electrical conduits, and in a variety of electrical uses. Indeed we can imagine a world in which copper is so expensive that it will be replaced by other metals for most of its present uses.

We can, then, foresee two important trends for the future, both intimately related to an ever more complex technology. As we move toward the processing of lower and lower grades of ore deposits, capital investments per unit of metal output must necessarily increase, as must also energy consumption per unit of output.

During the last few decades the changes in capital and energy investment per unit of output have been in quite the opposite direction—that is, they have decreased as a result of increasing mechanization and automation. Increased efficiency in the use of fuel has resulted in a steadily decreasing energy consumption per unit of output. But we are likely to see in the near future a reversal of these trends. And when the changes do take place it is likely that the increases in both capital investment and energy consumption per unit of industrial output will be steady and continuing ones which will extend far into the future.

Twelve

OUR ENERGY RESOURCES

We have seen that the question as to what constitutes an available raw material is in large part a question of energy. Since this is the case, let us examine the energy resources of the world and attempt to evaluate their adequacy on a long-range basis.

Since the beginnings of the Industrial Revolution, world production of coal has risen until it is now nearly 2 billion metric tons per year. Since the discovery of large reservoirs of petroleum and natural gas, an increasing proportion of the world's energy has been obtained from these new sources, in part due to the versatility of liquid and gaseous carbon compounds and in part as a result of their relative ease of extraction. World production of crude oil has now reached about 5 billion barrels annually, which is equivalent in energy content to about 1.2 billion tons of coal. Natural gas, in an amount equivalent in energy content to an additional 0.5 billion tons of coal, is marketed annually.

Thus from these three sources—coal, petroleum, and natural gas—we obtain each year an amount of energy equivalent to about 3.7 billion tons of coal, corresponding to nearly 1.4 tons of coal per capita. To this we should add an amount of coal corresponding to that which would be required to generate the electricity which we obtain from water power. This is very small, however. Although water power is very important in certain regions, it is relatively

negligible when we consider the world as a whole—we find that
the energy which it produces amounts to the equivalent of that
produced by less than 0.1 billion tons of coal annually.

If all the people of the world were to expend energy at the

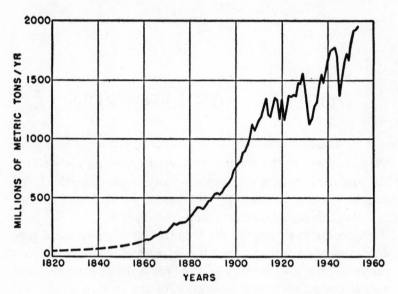

FIGURE 16

World Production of Coal

per capita rate at which we expend it in the United States, the total
rate of energy expenditure would increase approximately sixfold
to the equivalent of that contained in 22 billion tons of coal each
year. But in view of the fact that energy costs per unit of industrial
output are bound to climb considerably in the future, and that the
population of the world is destined to become considerably larger
than it is at present, world demands for energy could well exceed
this and could eventually approach the equivalent of 100 billion
tons annually. But could the energy resources available to us support such rapid expenditures for any appreciable length of time?

On the basis of our geological experience with coal, we now

have a reasonably clear picture concerning where it is, and where it is not to be found in the earth. Our experience has enabled geologists to make a number of estimates during the last few decades of the amount of coal which man may ultimately extract from the

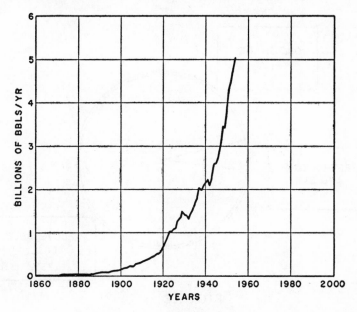

FIGURE 17

World Production of Crude Oil

earth. These estimates agree in suggesting that we may have available as much as 6000 billion tons. If we confine ourselves to those beds of coal which are neither too deep nor too thin, and if we assume a 50-per-cent loss in mining, we arrive at a somewhat lower figure, about 2500 billion tons, which would be sufficient to provide for the world's energy needs, at the current rate of expenditure, for about 700 years.

Similarly, during the last few years our knowledge concerning the occurrence of petroleum has been applied to the problem of estimating world-wide petroleum reserves. The results of recent investigations have been summarized by M. King Hubbert (see Notes), and it now appears that about 1250 billion barrels of oil may ultimately be extracted from the earth's crust. This is equivalent in energy content to about 280 billion tons of coal. We must

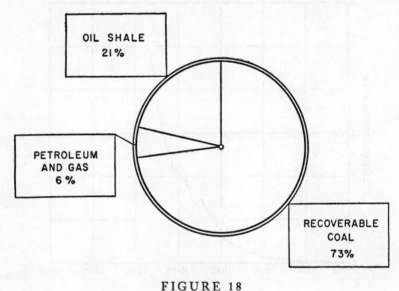

FIGURE 18

Reserves of Fossil Fuels

add to this the natural gas, which is genetically related to oil, and which may possess altogether as much energy as oil. We must also add the oil which might be extractable from shales and from tar sands throughout the world. The sum of these various sources of fossil fuels amounts to the equivalent of about 3700 billion tons of coal. Figure 18 shows the distribution of energy reserves among these various sources. It is clear that within this group of fuels coal constitutes by far our largest and most important reserve of energy.

Deposits of fossil fuels are finite and must therefore be ultimately exhausted. But long before this occurs they will become very difficult to obtain, as coal is mined from deeper and deeper levels and from progressively narrower veins. Production and consumption of fossil fuels will therefore pass through maxima (see Notes). The rise to the maximum for each fuel follows the law of compound interest, following our growing demand for energy. And because of the steepness of the rise, the position of the maximum in time is relatively insensitive to estimates of reserves.

In the world as a whole, approximately 90 billion barrels of crude oil have already been produced. We have proved reserves—a quantity of oil which we know to be available for tapping—amounting to about 250 billion barrels. It seems likely that an additional 900 or so billion barrels of petroleum await discovery. Nevertheless, so rapid is the rise in the demand for liquid fuels, by the end of the twentieth century the world as a whole will probably pass through its peak of crude-oil production. Indeed, should the level of world petroleum production rise to more than about two and one-half times the present level of production, the peak may well occur before the next century appears.

When we consider the rapidity with which demands for energy are increasing, the quantities of fuels which are available in shales and in tar sands, though important, are not impressive. Coal is clearly our major fossil fuel, and it is destined to remain the major source of energy for the world for some time to come.

We appear, then, to have a total of fossil fuels which is equivalent to perhaps 3700 billion tons of coal. At current rates of expenditure this should be sufficient to last for another thousand years. But, as we have seen, the rate of consumption is destined to increase considerably in the decades ahead and, were there sufficient fuel, a twenty-five-fold increase in consumption would not be out of the question. Clearly, if we were to consume energy at such a greatly accelerated rate, our fossil fuels would not last very long. Indeed, at a twenty-five times greater rate of consumption they would last only another forty years!

We must conclude, then, that although the age of fossil fuels has barely begun, we can already see its end. We must soon learn to utilize other, more permanent sources of energy, and we must recognize that, once our petroleum and coal have been consumed, as far as the human species is concerned, they will have disappeared forever.

For the years ahead, we can anticipate major changes in the patterns of fossil-fuel consumption in the world. Liquid fuels, because of their convenience and versatility, will continue to be in major demand, but the sources of supply will change. As we approach the limits of the earth's petroleum reserves and as the cost of petroleum increases, the extraction of hydrocarbons from oil shales and from tar sands will become feasible. These, however, will not last very long, for by that time world demands for liquid fuels will be very much higher than they are today. We will then begin on a large scale to produce liquid fuels by coal hydrogenation (the addition of hydrogen to coal). This will be energetically expensive, for there will be many energy losses in the process. Eventually, however, practically all liquid fuels will be produced from coal. And coal will be the major raw material for the chemical and plastics industries.

These changes in patterns of energy consumption will take place unevenly throughout the world as a result of the unevenness of the distribution of fossil fuels and differences in the rate of technological advance. Thus, the United States, which consumes liquid fuels at an extremely rapid rate, will undoubtedly pass through its peak of domestic petroleum production at a considerably earlier date than will the world as a whole—perhaps as early as 1965-70. As we approach the depletion of our domestic reserves, a very real question will arise concerning the extent to which we permit ourselves to become dependent upon imports of petroleum from abroad. In any event, however, it seems highly probable that by the end of the century we will be hydrogenating coal on a very large scale.

Coal is distributed unevenly through the world, and when we put estimated coal reserves on a per capita basis the disparities between certain major regions become even more pronounced. Thus the United States on a per capita basis has huge reserves—sufficient, at present rates of energy expenditure, to last several centuries. By contrast, were India to consume energy at our per capita rate, her reserves would last little more than ten years, and all of South and

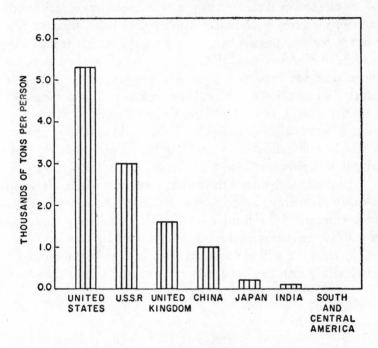

FIGURE 19

Probable Reserve of Extractable Coal per Capita

Central America could survive for little more than a year at the United States rate of energy consumption.

Thus it is clear that in areas such as India and South America the industrial transition cannot be completed with existing energy reserves. Reserves of coal in India are very important from the point of view of starting the industrialization process, but long before India attains a per capita level of energy expenditure which even remotely approaches that characteristic of the West today, it will be necessary for her to utilize new sources of energy. And in the greater part of South America it would appear that new energy sources are necessary if the industrialization process is even to be started.

Severe energy difficulties can be experienced by countries with per capita reserves much higher than those of India. Japanese coal reserves, for example, are of poor quality and are not readily susceptible to mechanization. With a large part of her hydroelectric potential already developed, Japan is finding it necessary to import substantial quantities of energy. Western Europe is importing coal from the United States. Even the United Kingdom, which possesses the most extensive coal fields in the world in relation to area, is experiencing difficulties in satisfying her energy needs. As a result she is already searching for other sources of energy.

Thus, although there is theoretically sufficient coal in the world to satisfy the energy requirements of mankind for a very long time, the unevenness of the distribution of fossil fuels already confronts us with severe energy problems. As time goes by these problems will increase and will undoubtedly stimulate the expansion of research efforts aimed at the development of new energy sources.

Thirteen

NEW KNOWLEDGE AND
NEW ENERGY

If the energy consumption of the world were to increase no further, mankind could probably maintain its present level of productivity for an indefinitely long period of time—even after resources of fossil fuels had disappeared—simply by developing all potential water-power resources and by harvesting all the world's forests on a sustained-yield basis. But if rates of energy consumption continue to accelerate, and reach the levels we have seen to be probable, and if these rates are maintained beyond the time when our supplies of petroleum and coal are exhausted, it will be necessary for man to make use of new, less conventional sources of energy.

When we survey the energy sources which are potentially available, we find that forms such as earth heat, winds, and tides can be, at best, of limited usefulness. There are a few localities where such sources are being tapped today, and there are others where they might be tapped economically in the future. But when we assess the total energy output which might eventually be developed economically from such sources it turns out to be very small compared to eventual world-wide demand.

Indeed, from a long-range point of view it is apparent that we must eventually depend more and more upon solar energy and nuclear energy. We now know that from the technological point of view both of these can be utilized. The question as to which will be most widely used is a question of economics. Which will require the least capital investment per unit of output? Which will have the lowest operating cost? On the basis of what we now know about the technologies of utilizing these two forms of energy it appears that for the generation of mechanical power and electricity, nuclear energy will probably be less expensive than solar by a considerable margin.

A number of systems have been devised for transforming solar heat into electricity, but the capital costs per unit of capacity have in all cases been extremely high. In hot regions the sun's energy might be used essentially to replace fossil fuels for the heating of water in an electrical generation plant. In order to accomplish this, the sun's rays are captured by special flat-plate collectors. Capital costs might run to $20,000 per acre; and the resultant power, depending upon the efficiency of the system, might cost several cents per kilowatt-hour, compared with prevailing costs of generating electricity, of a few mills per kilowatt-hour.

We also know that electricity can be generated by allowing the sun's radiation to fall upon semi-conductors. This phenomenon is now being put to good use in the Bell "solar battery," which can be used to generate electricity for a variety of small-scale uses. The large-scale use of this method would, however, involve prohibitively high capital costs. Other systems for the direct conversion of solar energy into electricity present the same difficulty.

One of the most efficient and least expensive means of producing mechanical and electrical energy from solar energy is to grow trees in the sun, to harvest the wood, and then to burn the wood in the firebox of a boiler. Or one can ferment sugar, which can be obtained in high yield per acre by growing cane or sugar beets, and thus obtain alcohol or a variety of combustible gases and liquids which can be used for generating power. But in view of the pressure on the world's agriculture to produce food and the probability that the food shortage will continue for a considerable time in the future, it is unlikely that much potential agricultural land will be diverted to the production of fuels.

An ingenious system has recently been described for the production of power from algae grown in a closed system containing a high concentration of carbon dioxide. The algae are cultured and then fermented in such a way that methane and hydrogen are produced. These gases are burned in a gas turbine or engine which is used to generate electricity. The carbon dioxide which results from the combustion is returned to the algae culture unit. In this way, under ideal conditions, one would have a closed system which would convert between 1 per cent and 3 per cent of the incident solar energy into electricity. It has been estimated that a system of this general type could be used to produce electricity at a cost of 2.5 to 5 cents per kilowatt-hour, and liquid fuels at a cost of about $150 per ton (see Notes).

Although it is doubtful that solar energy can compete with nuclear energy for the large-scale generation of power, there are areas where it will probably turn out to be very useful on a smaller scale. We have already mentioned the solar battery. Solar water heaters are coming into widespread use in tropical regions. An inexpensive solar cooker has been devised in the National Physical Laboratory in India; this could, if widely used, bring about the saving of substantial quantities of fuel. At the same laboratory a solar pump has been devised which could be used for pumping water on a small scale in isolated regions where fuels are not available.

It is likely that the most important use for solar energy in the future, however, will be for space heating. We now know that houses can be designed in such a way that requirements for space heating could be met almost entirely by solar energy in populated regions of the world as far north as Boston. The additional capital costs which would be required in house construction do not permit these techniques to be used widely at the present time. But as the prices of conventional fuels increase we will probably approach the time when most buildings will be designed to make maximum use of solar heat.

It is now reasonably certain that electricity can eventually be produced from nuclear energy at costs which are less than 1 cent (10 mills) per kilowatt-hour. How much lower than 10 mills the cost can become, and how rapidly, are matters for conjecture. At the International Conference on the Peaceful Uses of Atomic Energy, which was held in Geneva in 1955, estimates as low as 4 mills per kilowatt-hour were given. Forecasts of the eventual nuclear-power-generating costs in the United States range from 4 to somewhat over 6 mills per kilowatt-hour. Sapir and Van Hyning, in their study on the outlook for nuclear power in Japan, have reviewed the evidence and made the reasonable assumption that we might have available 10-mill nuclear power by the mid 1960s, 7-mill power by the mid 1970s, with the cost gradually approaching 5 mills per kilowatt-hour. These estimates can be compared with generating costs of between 6 and 7 mills per kilowatt-hour for new coal-fired units in the United States and about 18 mills for similar plants in Japan.

It is likely, then, that nuclear electricity will compete with that generated from coal in the not too distant future. And it seems clear that this competition will take place unevenly throughout the world.

We saw earlier that the United States is richly endowed with coal and that our seams can be mined without great technical difficulty. On a per capita basis we have the largest coal reserves in the world, with the result that our country as a whole is not likely to encounter a fuel shortage for many decades. Our coal seams, however, are not uniformly distributed through the nation, and fuel costs increase as one moves away from the available supply. A number of areas which are far removed from coal fields—for example, Southern California—are at present able to generate power at reasonable prices from petroleum or natural gas. There are other areas, however, where both coal and petroleum are expensive and where power costs are, as a result, considerably higher than the national average. It is in these areas that nuclear power might be expected to play its first major role in the United States.

If, as seems quite possible, we pass through a peak of domestic petroleum production by about 1970, nuclear power may well become important in those areas, such as the Far West, which lack coal but which at present have ready access to adequate supplies of petroleum or natural gas. After 1970 or 1975 the domestic importance of nuclear power may well increase rather rapidly. If, as seems possible, we pass through the peak of world petroleum production in about 1990, demand for coal will increase sharply and nuclear energy will probably be able to compete economically on a fairly broad front. But the production costs of coal in the United States are so low that it seems likely that it will remain our major fuel for a very long time.

The situation in the greater part of the world differs considerably from that in the United States, largely because of the substantial differences in fuel costs which prevail. In the United States we are able to generate steam electric power at coal costs which average about $6 per ton. In Western Europe, by contrast, the cost ranges from $13 to $20 per ton. Coal averages about $20 per ton in the United Kingdom. Western Europe is paying $20 per ton at the dock for large quantities of American coal. When we take into account the fact that more than 50 per cent of the cost of generating electricity can be fuel cost, we can realize that nuclear electricity can probably compete with coal-generated electricity in other parts of the world long before it is competitive on a really broad base in the United States.

When we couple the fuel cost differential with two additional factors, the differences between the situation in the United States and that in other countries become even more dramatic. The first consideration is that of foreign exchange (see Notes). Those regions of the world which must look forward to continued heavy imports of fossil fuels, and which face balance-of-payment difficulties, may well prefer to generate nuclear power, even when it is more expensive than power generated from conventional sources, if by so doing they minimize the drain upon their domestic financial resources.

The second major factor involves the striving on the part of most nations for economic self-sufficiency. Supplies of petroleum are uncertain. A very large fraction of the world's potential oil reserves are in the Middle East, where they are sensitive to the status of international relationships. Many nations will prefer an assured supply of nuclear power at relatively high but decreasing prices to less expensive but uncertain supplies of crude oil at prices which are destined to continue increasing.

The Soviet Union appears to be a rather special case with respect to nuclear-energy needs. Although she has vast coal resources, most of the coal lies in Siberia, while in the European part of the country there is a fuel shortage. Each year, apparently, nearly 15 million tons of coal are shipped from Karaganda and Kazakhstan to European Russia—a distance of some 1500 to 2000 miles. This is one of the reasons the Soviet government has stressed the importance of the industrialization of Siberia. And it is one of the reasons it has announced the establishment of a program to build five new nuclear-electric plants in Moscow, Leningrad, and the Urals.

To sum up the situation, it seems clear that nuclear energy can play a major role in many regions of the world—particularly in Europe, South America, Southeast Asia, and Japan—just as soon as reactors are developed capable of producing power at costs of 10 mills per kilowatt-hour, or less. It is ironical that the United States, possessor of what is probably the world's most highly developed nuclear technology, has at the moment the least need for nuclear power, except for specialized military purposes. And the prospects are that, while our need will grow, it will grow considerably more slowly than will the needs of many other nations.

On the basis of the preceding discussion, let us now map out a possible but reasonable pattern of world energy consumption for the next century. Barring a world catastrophe, and assuming that industrialization will spread throughout the world, that population will continue to grow, and that we shall have adequate brainpower to solve our prodigious technical problems as they arise, total energy consumption will continue to rise rapidly, following the law of compound interest. During the next ten to twenty years consumption

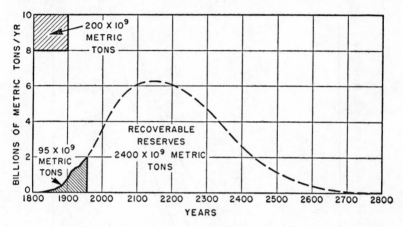

FIGURE 20

Ultimate World Coal Production

of petroleum will probably increase more rapidly than will the consumption of coal, but by about 1975 the rate of increase is likely to slacken so that the total rate of consumption will pass through a broad peak late in this century.

As the petroleum supplies diminish, increasing emphasis will be placed upon the production of liquid fuels from shales, tar sands, and coal hydrogenation. After about 1975 it seems likely that the gap between coal and petroleum as primary sources of energy will widen rather rapidly.

After about 1980 nuclear energy should represent a significant proportion of world power production, primarily as a replacement for fossil fuels in electrical power production. Its use should spread rather rapidly. By the end of the century nuclear energy may account for about one-third of our total energy consumption. During this period demand for coal will continue to increase, largely because of the continually increasing demand for liquid fuels and for a variety of complex chemicals. By the middle of the next century it seems likely that most of our energy needs will be satisfied

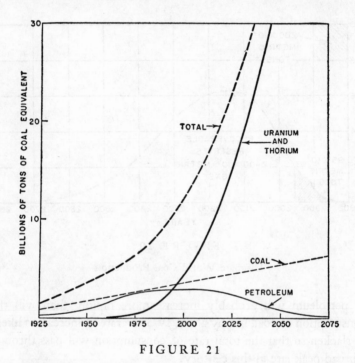

FIGURE 21

World Energy Consumption in the Next Century—a Possible Pattern

by nuclear energy, with coal reserved almost entirely for the production of liquid fuels and chemicals.

We must now ask how long we can expect the earth's supplies of uranium and thorium to power an industrial world. These elements, like coal and petroleum, are fossil fuels; they were made when the elements were formed, and they are not being made at the present time. The quantities of uranium and thorium which are available to us are, then, finite. Nevertheless, the energy available to man in the form of uranium and thorium is enormously greater than the energy contained in our reserves of coal and petroleum. This is because uranium and thorium are found in low but significant quantities in the common rocks of the earth's crust.

An average piece of granite contains only about 4 parts per million of uranium and about 12 parts per million of thorium. These are indeed small quantities, yet the uranium and thorium in 1 ton of average granite contains energy equivalent to about 50 tons of coal. Of course, not all this energy is available, as the process of extracting the elements from the rock necessitates a substantial energy expenditure. Energy is consumed in quarrying, crushing, and grinding the rock, in transporting the rock to the chemical plant, in making the chemicals which are used in processing, and in the manufacture of the processing equipment. Clearly if the energy required to extract the uranium and thorium were as great as the energy content of the extracted material, there would be no profit.

It has been found, however, that about one-third of the uranium and thorium is localized within the rock in such a way that it can be extracted with very little expenditure of energy. Thus, from 1 ton of ordinary granite, energy which is equivalent to about 15 tons of coal can be economically extracted. This means that from the long-range point of view man need not be confined to high-grade uranium and thorium ores for his energy. He will be able, if need be, to extract his energy needs from the very rocks of the earth's crust. And, as we saw earlier, the same rocks can supply the variety of metals which are necessary for the perpetuation of a highly industrialized civilization.

There is, in the long run, the possibility of producing power from thermonuclear reactions—from fusion of hydrogen as distinct from fission of uranium. No one as yet sees very clearly just how this is to be done, but it is nevertheless a very real possibility. If the technical problems are solved, the waters of the seas will be available to man as an almost infinite source of energy. This new energy may well be more expensive than that obtained from uranium fission. Nevertheless it also may be available for tapping when it is needed, at some distant time.

It is interesting to speculate about the pattern of energy consumption in a highly industrialized world, a world in the distant future when all fossil fuels have been consumed. Let us assume that human beings learn to regulate their numbers and that the population of the world is eventually stabilized at about 7 billion persons. Let us assume further that energy requirements amount to the equivalent of 10 tons of coal per person. This would be larger than the present per capita consumption of energy in the United States. But it should be emphasized that the per capita flow of goods would be considerably less than at present, for the reason that all goods would be more expensive, in terms of energy needed to produce them, than they are today. The total energy requirements for this society would amount to the equivalent of 70 billion tons of coal annually. We can assume that by then solar energy is being used wherever possible for space heating. We can assume further that all potential hydroelectric sources have been developed and that the world's forests are developed and harvested on a self-sustaining basis. Under these circumstances about 65 per cent of the total energy needs would be satisfied by nuclear energy, as is shown in Table VI.

In conclusion, it seems clear that man has available potential sources of energy which are sufficient to satisfy his needs for a very long time. However, these resources have yet to be transformed from potential supplies into actual ones. Before they can be used they must be developed. Whether or not man will be able to develop them in time is a very real question, the answer to which will be determined, in the long run, by many factors of a political, economic, and social nature.

TABLE VI. *Possible Pattern of Energy Consumption with World Population of Seven Billion*

(*Total energy requirement assumed to be 70 billion metric tons of coal or equivalent annually*)

SOURCE	EQUIVALENT METRIC TONS OF COAL (BILLIONS)
Solar energy (for two-thirds of space heating)	15.6
Hydroelectricity	4.2
Wood for lumber and paper	2.7
Wood for conversion to liquid fuels and chemicals	2.3
Liquid fuels and "petro" chemicals produced via nuclear energy	10.0
Nuclear electricity	35.2
Total	70.0

Fourteen

TECHNICAL MANPOWER,
PRESENT AND FUTURE

In our analysis thus far of the material, energy, and food resources of the world, from the purely technological point of view the future of mankind seems secure, if we exclude the possibility of a world catastrophe. There is an almost infinite supply of raw materials and of energy in the granite of the earth's crust, and we have sufficient knowledge of the technology of agriculture and of food production to support a world population of several times our present one. In principle, we may think of the problem of food and material resources in terms of energy. If we can produce sufficient quantities of energy and expend it properly in the production of food and materials, we can meet the demands we foresee for the future. All we need do is add sufficient energy to the system and we can obtain whatever materials we desire.

Our only remaining problem, then, is how to add this energy to the system. Obviously, someone must do it. But this is by no means a simple matter—much skill, knowledge, and equipment is required, and additional skill and knowledge are needed to build the equipment. So, in effect, we may be limited in the amount of energy we can expend, or in the rate at which we can expend it, by the availability of this knowledge and skill—that is, by the availability of technical brainpower, of trained scientists and engineers. In order for us to have produced the vast quantities of raw materials, food, and energy that we discussed earlier, we have of necessity been forced to rely on the ingenuity, technical skill, and creative imagination of our engineers and scientists for the solution of many difficult technical problems. To attain our high level of production has required the accumulation of a great deal of knowledge, the training of sufficient numbers of scientists, engineers, and technicians, and the development of complex machines and systems. As populations increase, as individuals demand ever higher standards of living, and as we continue to expend more and more energy in the extraction of materials from lower- and lower-grade ores, it is inevitable that we will meet an ever mounting demand for this skilled technical brainpower—for more trained scientists and engineers. If we fail to develop this highly trained manpower in sufficient quantity we may find ourselves limited in the amount of energy we can expend or in the rate at which we can expend it. And so it appears that the critical limiting factor as far as the world's resources are concerned is not materials, energy, or food, but brainpower.

Let us, then, examine our present supply of scientists and engineers, and then attempt to arrive at an estimate of what future supply and demand might become.

At the present time the United States is the most complex industrialized society in the world. Since it offers almost unlimited educational opportunities of many different kinds, as well as great freedom of educational and vocational choice, an analysis of technical brainpower resources in America will provide us with a good example of the problems of supply and demand for engineers and scientists in a free economy.

Scientists and engineers have been in short supply in the United States for several years—a shortage which is growing more acute and to which no immediate end is in sight. So critical has it become that industrial organizations are curtailing research and development activities because of a lack of available trained men. The situation is especially alarming to those who hold the widespread opinion that continued growth and prosperity for many industries must come from sustained and vigorous research and development programs. The shortage of scientists and engineers has therefore become a subject of much concern, and vigorous and thoughtful efforts are being directed toward its alleviation. It is, however, a difficult problem and one that cannot be solved in a short time. It takes many years to train an engineer and even more to develop a professional scientist. Even if we were to double enrollments in technical colleges immediately, it would be five to ten years before an appreciable effect would be felt in the field or in the research laboratory.

Moreover, opinions differ as to the true cause of the present shortage. Some believe that it is the low birth rate of the depression years and the resultant decline in college enrollment in the early 1950s. Some believe that an abnormally increased demand for technical manpower has resulted from heavy defense spending. We shall see, however, that the shortage is the result of the rapidly increasing technical complexity of the United States economy and the failure of present methods of training technical manpower to keep up with our present needs. This conclusion implies that we may expect the shortage to continue and to become even more severe with the passage of time.

When we attempt to calculate the future supply of technical manpower, we are immediately faced with the problem of definition. What is a technician? What kinds of technologists should be included in such a tabulation? The answers to these questions are not easy to provide, for in an industrial network as complex as that of the United States there is a gradient of technical competence among workers that runs the gamut from the highly educated Ph. D., who is thoroughly familiar with the most recent and esoteric abstractions of modern science, down through the M. S., the B. S., and the high-school graduate, to the skilled mechanic who has learned his skills in a trade school or as an apprentice. Not only are there these differences in educational attainment, but there are other equally important gradations of experience and breadth of understanding. So there are truly many varieties of technologists, and any delimitation will be arbitrary. Nevertheless a delimitation must be made so that our analysis can be quantitative and meaningful.

For our purposes, it will be satisfactory to confine our discussion to those scientists and engineers who have obtained bachelors' degrees in their respective fields. There are several reasons why this is so. First, this particular group comprises the bulk of trained technical manpower in the United States. Second, a bachelor's degree in science or engineering provides a reasonably uniform criterion for professional competence.

The proportion of American youth that obtains bachelors' degrees has been increasing steadily in recent decades. In 1920 somewhat less than 3 per cent of all twenty-two-year-olds were college graduates. By 1930 this percentage doubled to almost 6 per cent. In 1940 it reached 8 per cent, and by 1950, 11 per cent. The rate of increase has slowed down in recent years, but it is predicted that by 1970 a plateau will be reached and that about 17 per cent of all twenty-two-year-olds in any one year will have earned college degrees.

For the past several decades the proportion of the graduates of any particular year that obtains degrees in engineering and science has remained around 18 to 22 per cent. Within this group of technical graduates, however, not all continue in their respective fields. In fact, the best estimates we have indicate that only about two-thirds of the engineers and one-third of the scientists actually do so.

Let us now use these varied facts to calculate our future supply of engineers and scientists. On the basis that 17 per cent of all twenty-two-year-olds will graduate from college, that 22 per cent will obtain degrees in science and engineering, and that one-third of the scientists and two-thirds of the engineers continue in their respective fields, we obtain the curve shown in Figure 22. It shows the total number of scientists and engineers with bachelors' degrees in the working population, and is adjusted for losses due to death and for retirement at sixty-five. It gives us our expected available supply of working engineers and scientists of this level of competence from now to the year 2000—based, of course, on the assumption that past trends will continue to the turn of the century. It is accurate to the year 1979, for we can calculate accurately how many twenty-two-year-olds will appear each year up to that time.

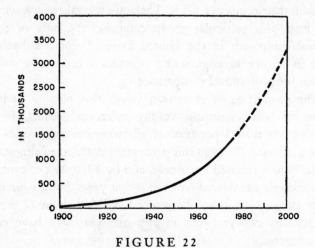

FIGURE 22

Number of Scientists and Engineers with Bachelors' Degrees in the Working Population

Conditions: 1. 17 per cent of 22-year-olds obtain first degrees. 2. 22 per cent obtain degrees in science and engineering. 3. 35 per cent of scientists and 65 per cent of engineers are in their technical fields.

The curve beyond 1979 is calculated on the basis of future population estimates made by the Census Bureau. Our curve forecasts that we will have about 1,700,000 engineers and scientists in the working population by 1980, and about 3,300,000 by the year 2000.

We have, then, our estimate of future supply. What will be the future demand? This is a much more difficult question to answer, for to forecast demand one should take into account future social, political, and technological changes—an impossibility at the present time. However, we can make a few estimates on the basis of past relationships.

For example, one indication of the growing technological complexity of the United States has been the increased amount of effort and money spent on research and development activities. It is obvious, of course, that not all scientists and engineers in the working population are engaged in research and development activities. Perhaps only about one-third of them are. Even so, today's industrial engineering is the result of yesterday's research findings, and in industrial and military research and development expenditures we have a measure that is at the very heart of technical activity.

It is noteworthy that the yearly percentage increase in research and development expenditures has been constant for several decades. Further, the ratio between research and development expenditures and the total number of working college-graduate engineers and scientists has been a constant one throughout the same period. If we assume that this ratio will hold to the end of the century, then we can estimate the total number of scientists and engineers that will be needed up to that time. The curve which results from this calculation is given in Figure 23, which includes the curve showing the number which we can expect to have available. A comparison of the two curves suggests that we may need about twice our available supply of technical manpower by 1982 and three times the supply by the end of the century.

We can estimate future demand by another and different approach. We discussed earlier the change in the composition of the American labor force during the past half-century, noting the decrease in the percentage of laborers and unskilled workers and the increase in the percentage of semiskilled and professional workers. The greater part of the increase in the proportion of professional workers is due primarily to increased numbers of scientists and engineers. As a consequence, the ratio of population to engineers and scientists in the United States has become smaller and smaller. This change in ratio has actually been a very rapid one. If we plot the number of people per engineer or scientist in the United States against time, we obtain the curve shown in Figure 24. It is evident that the number of people per working scientist or engineer has decreased more and more rapidly since 1900. At the beginning of

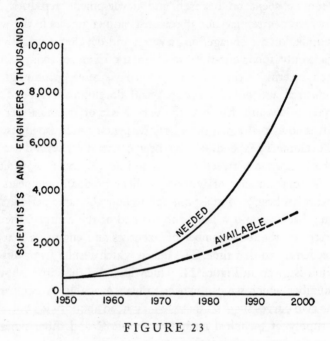

FIGURE 23

Projected Technical Manpower Needs
(Based on research and development appropriations)

the twentieth century there were about 1800 persons in the United States for each working scientist or engineer. By 1950, the ratio was about 300 to 1. If these trends continue, we shall need by 1980 a number of scientists and engineers in the ratio of 1 to every 90 persons, and by the year 2000, 1 to every 40. When we compare this estimate of demand with the curve of supply, we may conclude that we will need over twice as many scientists and engineers as we will have available in the year 2000.

These two independent estimates of future demand are similar in suggesting that we will need perhaps twice as many engineers and scientists as we will have available by the year 1980 and about three times as many by the end of the century. The time has apparently come when we can no longer meet our increasing demand

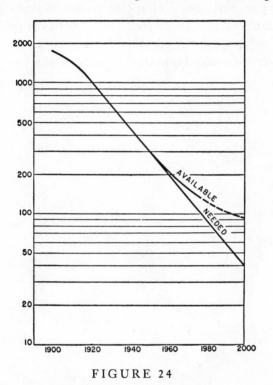

FIGURE 24

Projected Technical Manpower Needs
(Based on U.S. population per degree-holding engineer or
scientist working in the field)

for technical brainpower from our present sources of supply. The current shortage seems to be but the beginning of a new and extended era in industrial civilization characterized by chronic shortages of scientific and engineering manpower.

These considerations immediately raise the central question in our analysis of future technical-manpower resources. What are our ultimate potential resources of trained men? If we were able to change these past trends, could we increase the number of scientists and engineers produced each year? If so, by how many?

During each half-century since 1800, both our yearly production and our total supply of engineers and scientists have been multiplied ten times. Can we continue to do this in the next half-century and beyond? Or are there finite limits to our technical-brainpower resources? These are the questions which we must now consider.

Fifteen

THE PRODUCTION OF SCIENTISTS
AND ENGINEERS

How many scientists and engineers can the United States produce? This is in part a question of the efficiency with which we can develop the potential engineers and scientists among our young people of school age. If we are efficient in this matter, then every American youth who possesses the abilities, traits, and characteristics required of successful scientists and engineers and who wishes to enter these fields will do so and will develop his potential abilities to their fullest extent. To the degree that there are capable or talented young people who do not develop and use their abilities to the fullest extent, we are inefficient.

As we are limiting our considerations here to engineers and scientists who have obtained bachelors' degrees from college or university, we can readily assess how well we are doing in the education of our young people by studying college enrollment and graduation figures. For example, let us take a random sample of one hundred American youths and follow them through their educational careers. Figure 25 shows the educational levels they will attain. All of them will enter the first grade, since in America everyone goes to school. Eighty will begin the ninth grade, sixty the eleventh grade, and fifty-nine will graduate from high school.

Twenty of them will go on to college, from which thirteen will graduate—three in engineering and science. Only about one-third of our high-school graduates go on to college. Of those who do, slightly more than one-half obtain their bachelors' degrees.

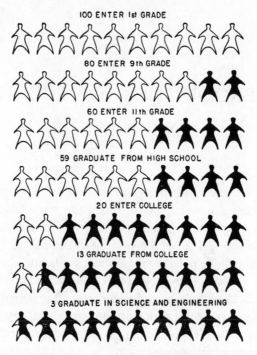

FIGURE 25

Attrition at Given Educational Levels in the United States

These figures, which are typical of recent decades, give some indication of the attrition among American young people as they progress up through various levels of educational achievement. But they do not tell the whole story, for one may quite appropriately ask: Should *all* high school graduates go to college? Or, Should *all* those who enter college obtain bachelors' degrees? The scholastic requirements set by our colleges and universities demand a minimum level of intellectual ability, so we must consider our output of intellectual manpower in terms of the available supply of potential graduates. We must concern ourselves with different levels of intellectual ability and judge how successful we are in helping each individual develop to his maximum potential.

Of course, intellectual ability is not the sole requirement for success in college work; there are many other important factors, such as motivation, socio-economic position, and finances. We have more to say about these matters later, but let us first examine the amounts of education acquired by young people of different intellectual capacities. This will give us a reasonable estimate of our educational efficiency, since intellectual ability is a fundamental prerequisite for scholastic attainment and differing degrees of ability are necessary in order to attain different levels of education. Figure 26 shows the distribution of intellectual ability among certain groups of American young people. The numbers on the horizontal scale represent scores on the Army General Classification Test. These scores are measures of intellectual ability and are roughly equivalent to Intelligence Quotients. The height of the curve above any scale score represents the relative frequency of occurrence of individuals with that degree of intellectual capacity. The large curve represents the distribution of intellectual ability within an entire age group in the United States. The next smaller curve represents the distribution of intellectual ability in that portion of the total group that graduates from high school. Next is shown the distribution of ability of the portion that enters college, then of the portion that graduates from college, and finally, of graduates from college with degrees in engineering or science.

These curves show quite clearly the importance of higher levels of intellectual ability for higher educational achievement. While the average intellectual capacity for the entire group is 100, it is 110 for high-school graduates, 115 for college entrants, and 120 for college graduates. But these curves also indicate that there must be important factors in addition to intellectual ability that determine success or failure in college. For on one hand, some

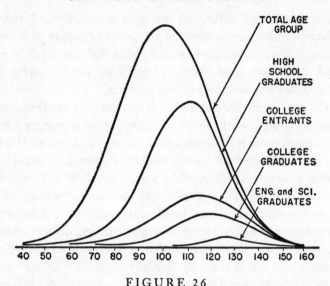

FIGURE 26

Distributions of Ability (AGCT Scores) of a Current Age
Group and of Those Reaching Different Educational Levels

young people scoring as low as 90 obtain college degrees, while
on the other hand, at the extremely high-ability end of the curve,
those with scale score 140 and above, we see that only two out
of three obtain college degrees. It is quite apparent that it takes
more than sheer intellectual ability to complete a college education.

These curves indicate rather dramatically that we fall far short
of developing to the fullest our intellectual resources within the
United States. If we assume, for example, that a score of 110 represents a reasonable minimum of intellectual ability necessary for
college-level work, then we can conclude that we lose two-thirds
of our potential college graduates. We lose, by the mere fact that
they don't go to college, one-half of the very capable and one-
third of the exceptionally talented.

Here, then, is one domain in which we might seek to increase
our output of intellectual and technical manpower. If we could

increase the efficiency of our educational procedures by eliminating this wasted potential brainpower, we could achieve an important reduction in our current technical-manpower shortage. Let us therefore look more closely at some of the factors which contribute to this waste, and then ask ourselves what our technical-manpower resources would be if we could eliminate most or all of it.

The problem of educational attrition from elementary school through college is a very complicated one. There are many known contributing causes, some simple and some complex. Some are well understood, some only slightly so. For our present purposes it is not necessary to compile an exhaustive list of them, nor do we need to go into any of them in great detail. A brief discussion of some of the more important factors will, however, help to define the problem and the magnitude of the effort that will be necessary to solve it.

The more important influences which lead to success or failure in the making of a scientist or engineer fall readily into three groups —namely, early identification, encouragement, and training. Let us consider briefly each of these.

Clearly, the earlier we can identify the embryo scientist or engineer the better, for we are then in a position to provide him with optimum intellectual and emotional opportunities and encouragement. He can then be provided with the specialized class and laboratory courses that will enable him to gain breadth of view and depth of understanding at his own pace. The psychological study of successful scientists and engineers has highlighted the importance of providing at as early an age as possible opportunities for extra laboratory work, field trips, special research projects, and freedom to explore new fields. There are some indications at the present time that occupational choice within broad fields is determined to a very significant extent by psychological and cultural influences such as the parents' occupations, the socio-economic status of the family, position of birth order among siblings, the attitudes of the parents toward intellectual knowledge, and the parents' own educational attainments. We are just beginning to understand the manner in which these influences work. As we gain more understanding, we will be able to identify the embryo scientist or engineer at a much earlier age than is now possible.

There is a widely held opinion among educational and vocational counselors that successful people in a particular occupational group have in common more or less specific and identifiable patterns of mental traits and abilities, which are different from the traits and abilities of other groups. For example, salesmen, writers, technologists, accountants, and personnel administrators each possess their own rather distinct pattern of aptitudes, abilities, interests, and values by which they can be characterized. Some of the traits and aptitudes that make up these patterns appear to have a large hereditary component and appear at a very early age. Many of the interests and values develop early in life, often making their appearance long before junior high school. Thus, any increased knowledge of how and for what reasons these patterns form will help lower the age at which we can identify the potential scientist or engineer. It will also increase our success in making this early identification, and this will be all to the good, for the earlier these identifications can be made, the less the likelihood of improper vocational choice or missed opportunities on the part of student and society.

The second group of problems centers around the encouragement of the budding scientist or engineer. Of importance here is his motivation for continued study and education. About half of the extremely high-ability students who fail to go on to college do so because they simply have no interest in higher education. A college education does not seem essential or desirable either to them or to their families. Often the young student's rejection of intellectual achievement is a result of attitudes toward intellectual knowledge held by his parents and his peers. And certainly with the great variety of social and cultural activities that are provided in American secondary schools today, distractions by competing interests and activities sorely test the student's motivation for intellectual work. It is quite easy for a young high-school student to be lured away from a study program that is as challenging and as demanding as is science or mathematics.

At both the elementary-school level and the high-school level, the manner in which science and mathematics are taught and the enthusiasm and understanding of the teacher often have tremendous influence in awakening the spark of curiosity in young students. Too often, unfortunately, teaching procedures and course requirements deaden any interest the young student may have brought to the subject. In a recent study, the Educational Testing Service observed sixty mathematics teachers at the elementary- and secondary-school level. It was found that only ten were competent to teach mathematics. The remaining fifty were judged to be confused, often dissatisfied, and unable to teach the subject except in a dull mechanical way. Many of them resented having to teach mathematics to classes of thirty-five to forty pupils who sometimes spread over two different grade levels and ranged from the bright but bored to the dull and bewildered. In a sense, there is some justification for this as an emergency measure to cope with the current shortage of mathematics teachers. But it unfortunately means that the young student's introduction to mathematics is one least likely to arouse and maintain his interest in the subject. This is a serious matter, since mathematics is fundamental to all study of science and engineering.

In the biographies of successful scientists and engineers there occurs over and over again the figure of some science or mathematics teacher who inspired the young students and kindled fires of enthusiasm that lasted for a lifetime. This kind of teacher is rare, for he possesses a combination of unusual qualities. He likes young people, and they like him. He is dedicated to teaching. He is well grounded in his subject and takes a professional interest in his field. He usually possesses an advanced degree. He is imaginative, enthusiastic, and hard-working. These are qualities for which industry can and will pay more than twice the salary paid by a school board today. As a result, the inspiring teacher must accept a great sacrifice in order to continue his teaching. Many more such teachers are needed if we are to increase our production of highly trained technical people.

Next, there is the matter of sound educational and vocational guidance and counseling. A student of high-school age is usually quite ignorant of the skills, abilities, interests, and personality traits which are necessary in order to be successful in a particular adult occupation. This is especially true for the professional occupations. Yet only rarely can a young student gain any first-hand experience as a scientist or engineer until very late in his college career. And so he must rely on the advice and guidance of others in making his vocational choice. Often he must begin this reliance in the tenth or eleventh grade in high school, at which time he must choose to study the mathematics and science courses that are required for admission to a technical school. He is much more likely to choose an occupation that will properly match his abilities, interests, and values if he has the opportunity to consider all possibilities in the course of discussions with trained counselors.

Still another influence that relates to the encouragement of potential scientists and engineers concerns financial support. In recent years about 40 per cent of high-school graduates who were clearly capable of doing college work did not go on to college because of lack of adequate finances. This is today recognized across the country as a loss of technical manpower that can be decreased by immediate and direct action. As a result the funds available for scholarship purposes have recently been increasing rapidly, especially in technical schools. They have come from school funds, from industry, and from state and federal programs. The time is approaching when any qualified and deserving high-school graduate who wishes to enter a technical field will not be blocked by lack of funds—whether he be merely capable, outstanding, or extremely gifted.

The third group of factors which affect losses in the production of engineers and scientists relates to training or education. First, there is the matter of the teaching staff, especially at the secondary-school level. We have already mentioned the inadequate training and deplorable attitudes toward the subject-matter which have been found in the survey of secondary-school mathematics teachers. This condition is not limited to mathematics teachers, but often applies as well to science teachers. Too frequently the criteria for teacher certification and promotion emphasize the number of education courses completed, at the expense of knowledge and interest in the subject-matter to be taught. As a consequence, one often finds high-school chemistry or physics teachers who have had only one or two years of study in their field. Yet there is convincing evidence that the inspiring science teacher is not of this kind. He is usually a person who has majored in his science subject in college, who has an advanced degree, and who has the same sort of professional interest in his field as do practicing scientists. It is probably impossible to be an inspiring teacher of a subject in which one has little knowledge or interest.

We are faced also with the fact that high-school science and mathematics teachers are in short supply. There is at present an acute shortage of them that is daily growing more acute. For example, we needed about 7900 new mathematics and science teachers in 1954–55. Thirty-eight hundred actually completed training in the same period. Of this number, only 2100 actually entered teaching in the fall—filling about one-fourth of the total need.

This attrition is easily explained. If the young teacher is well trained in his subject, he can begin his career in industry at an initial salary 25 to 50 per cent greater than the initial school salary. After five years in industry, he can expect to earn as much as the most he might earn after fourteen years in teaching. A qualified scientist must indeed be a dedicated teacher to resist such an attraction.

As a consequence of the increasing shortage of teachers, small high schools are often unable to offer courses in advanced mathematics, physics, and chemistry. A student at such a school who wishes to enter engineering or science cannot complete the high-school courses in mathematics and physics that are requirements for admission to most technical schools.

Thus, the over-all effect of these different influences on high-school science and mathematics teaching is to lower the quality of teaching and to make instruction in science and mathematics less available just at the time when our industrial growth demands more scientists and engineers.

There is no serious shortage of teaching staff in higher education—at least up to the present time. Higher pay scales, greater prestige, and opportunity to pursue individual research interests have so far proved sufficient to attract qualified scientists and engineers into university teaching. But it is quite possible that the coming tidal wave of increased enrollments now being felt in the elementary schools may inundate our technical colleges unless adequate preparations are made in time.

We can, however, increase our efficiency in the production of scientists and engineers at the college level by critically evaluating our admissions procedures and course requirements. Almost without exception, technical schools require of the applicant for admission a high-school diploma and high-school courses in mathematics, physics, and chemistry. This requirement is adhered to even though many college science and engineering professors maintain that high-school science is not only a waste of time but actually a hindrance to the student's further education. They contend that the college freshman must often first unlearn the misconceptions he has been taught in high school before he can learn modern science. Those who hold this view overlook, of course, the fact that high-school courses in science and mathematics form an essential part of the mechanism by which the student's interest is caught and channelized into a technical career.

One can certainly question, however, whether it is really necessary to take twenty-two years to develop a scientist or engineer to the bachelor's-degree level. Might it be feasible to push back the age at which college-level teaching is begun from eighteen to perhaps sixteen or fifteen? Are twelve years of elementary and secondary education necessary before the student is qualified to begin what we now regard as a college career? There is strong evidence that the answer is no. For example, a recent experiment financed by the Fund for the Advancement of Education, in which fifteen- and sixteen-year-old students were admitted to college after having completed only the tenth or eleventh grade of school, indicated that these accelerated students do just as well as and often better than their classmates who have completed high school in the conventional way before entering college. Their grades are generally satisfactory, and their interest in their studies is often greater than that of their contemporaries who have been exposed to the boredom which frequently accompanies a high-school education. Several reports have also indicated that students in well-planned and adequately staffed high-school science programs often produce scientific research and scholarly papers that are equal in quality to those done by college students. Elimination of the routine, trivial, and outmoded requirements carried over from traditional approaches to education could accelerate our production of scientists and engineers and at the same time make the process more satisfying and exciting to both student and teacher.

We also need to take a more critical look at our college course requirements. There have been almost no attempts to study the performance by college alumni in their productive careers and to find out how college performance and college course requirements prepare the student for later life. We have little validation of our college teaching procedures. In-company training programs are usually validated by measurements of the effect of the program on the efficiency or productivity of the employees. As a consequence, these training programs may be kept under constant surveillance and may be re-evaluated and reorganized if the evidence suggests the need for changes. But this is seldom if ever done in higher education. There are probably many undergraduate courses currently required of all students that make no useful contribution to the students' skill or knowledge either professionally, socially, or culturally. At the present time a college degree at the bachelor's level signifies success in conforming with college study requirements and grading procedures. But there is real question as to how much beyond this the college degree signifies.

The same conclusion is not true for the doctoral level of training, for here we still use the apprentice system, and the doctoral candidate learns scientific research by working with a scientist. What he studies and what he does directly relate and contribute to his development as a scientist or engineer. Under these circumstances we have almost continuous external validation of our teaching procedures. An appropriate validation of course requirements and teaching procedures at the undergraduate level would certainly help us to organize our teaching in such a way as to raise the quality of our graduates.

One might define modern education in terms of two broad objectives: 1) the learning of new facts and new skills; and 2) the development of the ability to synthesize these facts and skills into new patterns of thought and behavior. Psychologists and educators have spent many years of intensive effort in study of the learning process. A large body of knowledge has accumulated concerning both the principles and the practice of the teaching and learning of facts and skills. As a consequence, methods of teaching facts and training in skills and the results obtained have been improved continuously over many years. But we know very little about the principles of the synthesizing process—that is, about creative imagination or creative thinking. If we could acquire a broad understanding of the nature and nurture of the creative thought processes, if we could learn how to identify, how to measure, and how to develop them, we would add immeasurably to our brainpower resources.

We have discussed a few, but by no means all, of the major factors which currently limit the production of scientists and engineers in the United States. Some of the problems are quite obvious, and solutions to them appear simple and straightforward, although difficult to achieve. For example, the shortage of the science and mathematics teachers in the high schools would be eased if teacher pay scales were raised to the industrial level. Solutions to other problems are not so clear. It will take years of intensive research before we shall be able to enumerate all the important factors which contribute to the early identification of scientists and engineers, or before we understand thoroughly the nature of creative thought. It will take imagination, effort, and money to reduce these sources of waste to insignificance. However, if all these obstacles could be removed—and it seems theoretically possible to do so—then we would have a working force in which each individual would have achieved the highest educational level commensurate with his intellectual capacity. At the college level, this would mean all those in the total population with a scale score (on Figure 26) of 90 or 95. At the bachelor's level in science or engineering, it would mean 22 per cent of all those scoring above about 108. In terms of Figure 26, this would include all the people to the right of vertical lines drawn at these scale points. Clearly, we would greatly increase the number of college graduates produced each year. As a matter of fact, we would have graduated about 75,000 scientists and engineers each year for the last two years, instead of the 45,000 we actually did produce. We would have approximately doubled our output, and this doubling would not have been at the expense of other professions or other occupations. There would have been twice as many graduates in all fields of study. Moreover, they would have been better trained, more interested in their fields, more creative, and more likely to work at their full capacity. There are certainly ample rewards to be gained from an intensive and sustained effort to increase our efficiency in the production of engineers and scientists in the United States today.

We can also increase our production of scientists and engineers in quite another way. Among working college-graduate engineers and scientists in the United States, only 1 per cent of the engineers and 11 per cent of the scientists are women. Does this have to be? Are women different from men in some psychological or emotional characteristic that makes them incapable of becoming competent scientists and engineers? This does not appear to be the case. No student of human behavior has as yet convincingly isolated any difference between the sexes that would forever preclude women from becoming competent in these fields. In the elementary schools, and to a somewhat lesser extent in the high schools, girls are as frequently outstanding science students as are boys. Certainly there are social prejudices, attitudes, and value systems currently held by both sexes which prevent women from becoming engineers and scientists in greater numbers. But these are social and cultural in origin. They are learned, in the same manner as religious beliefs and political beliefs are learned, and so they can be changed. In Russia today, where 50 per cent of professional workers and at least 20 per cent of engineers are women, we have a clear demonstration that women can successfully enter these fields. If technical occupations were to be made available and attractive to women, then we might almost double again the number of scientists and engineers produced in America each year.

Sixteen

INCREASING
OUR BRAINPOWER OUTPUT

We have assessed technical-manpower resources from the standpoint of the production of new scientists and engineers. But the production of more technologists is only one of the ways in which we might hope to cope with the continually increasing technical complexity of the future. What we require is measured not by technical manpower, but by technical brainpower, and this is a function not only of the numbers of scientists and engineers available, but also of the quality and quantity of output of each individual. So let us now turn our attention to matters affecting the output of scientists and engineers after they have been trained—to a consideration of their utilization. Each time the individual scientist or engineer is utilized more effectively, each time his output is increased, we have increased our total brainpower resource.

One way in which scientists and engineers can be utilized more effectively is by confining their work more nearly to the field of their specialization. There are many ways that this can be done. Studies of the manner in which the working hours of scientists and engineers are spent immediately suggest several avenues of approach. They can be freed from administrative detail, from unnecessary paper work, and from semi-technical or subprofessional work that could be done just as well by technicians who are not so highly trained. Fewer would be diverted into executive positions in industry and government if the yearly pay of high-quality research workers were to be made equal to that of high-quality business executives. And undoubtedly much could be accomplished by a strict surveillance of our military manpower policies, to insure that highly trained technical men are not drafted from essential technical activities, merely to be used less effectively or non-technically within the armed forces. The importance of this consideration is indicated by the fact that 22 per cent of the 1956 class of engineering graduates will be commissioned in the ROTC for duty tours of from one to three years. Most of the remaining 78 per cent are destined for military duty of some sort.

Another approach to increasing the productivity of technical people is through improvements in communication. Optimal communication between individuals and between working technical groups is essential if a free flow of ideas is to be maintained. Studies of group dynamics have demonstrated in recent years that interpersonal communication, the transfer of a mental image or idea from one person to another, is a complex process in which each participant unconsciously censors both what he says and what he hears. Science and engineering education at present seldom includes a sophisticated program designed to develop communication skills, although the value of these skills is becoming increasingly evident. Communication skills may also be developed through training on the job. The results of such training programs indicate that they are entirely feasible and produce worth-while results. Our technical brainpower resources will certainly be increased as we develop the skills and mechanisms for maximum communication.

Another avenue for increasing productivity has to do with the way in which scientists and engineers are rewarded. We have noted earlier that successful scientists and engineers possess a pattern of mental abilities, interests, and personality characteristics which distinguishes them from other occupational groups. This view carries the implication that the motives which led scientists and engineers to choose their vocation are to some extent also unique and characteristic. This in turn suggests there may be incentives and rewards that are especially appropriate for the motivation of scientists and engineers. It implies that incentives and rewards may be tailored in very specific ways to meet the characteristic psychological and emotional needs of this group. Certainly salary and general working conditions are of importance to them, as they are to other occupational groups. But there are additional rewards of importance to the technical person. These include adequate facilities and equipment; reward for intellectual achievement; awards such as medals, citations, and sabbatical leave; opportunity to do independent research of his choosing and on his own problems; encouragement to pursue further study; and provision for easy access to current books and periodicals in his field. Additional important rewards might consist in opportunities to discuss professional matters with leaders in his field; time and expenses to attend professional meetings to present papers; and special rewards for membership or leadership in professional organizations.

Designing of laboratory organization to harmonize with the interest patterns and value systems of its technical staff can have an important influence on the productive output of its professional people. A recent morale survey conducted by the University of Chicago's Industrial Relations Center revealed important dissatisfactions with present laboratory organization among engineers and scientists in industry today. The hierarchical organization pattern that is typical of most of industry does not work well when applied to the research laboratory. An organizational arrangement of colleagues, such as is typical of universities and research institutes, is much more compatible with the needs and requirements of scientists and engineers. In this setting leadership develops informally and is based on the ability of the individual scientist as judged by his colleagues. In the colleague or academic type of organization there is also greater freedom for communication and exchange of ideas than in the hierarchical pattern, and much less likelihood that department heads will attempt to appropriate the ideas of their technical staffs.

These, then, are some of the ways in which the utilization, the motivation, and the effectiveness of trained scientists and engineers can be increased. There is still a further avenue for increasing the output of our technical manpower, an avenue that may be the most important one of all. This has to do with creative imagination. Certainly one of the most valuable elements in any productive activity is the generation of new ideas and of new solutions to old problems. Unfortunately, as we have already seen, very little is known about the psychology of creative imagination. In recent years, however, research psychologists have become interested in this question, and some tentative conclusions are being drawn.

We are beginning to identify some of the factors that are important in facilitating creative thinking. We are beginning to develop procedures and techniques that help to stimulate creativity in individuals, in groups, and in companies. There is, for example, the technique known as "brainstorming." In this procedure a group meets under conditions designed to make it easy for its members to express their ideas without fear of ridicule or criticism. It is quite effective in increasing the output of new ideas from people brought together for the purpose. Brainstorming has been used successfully in advertising, sales, production, and management. It can be used with equal effectiveness in research and development, and in fact in any activity in which the generation of new or different ideas is the goal. A few industrial and governmental organizations have made determined efforts to increase the creative output of their employees, both as individuals and in groups. Others have tried to organize their laboratories in such a way as to stimulate and facilitate creative thinking. The result has in general been a noticeable increase in creative productivity. And this is just a start. What we now do on a small scale and with inadequate knowledge we can hope to do in the future on a much larger scale and on a more rational basis.

These, then, are some of the important factors that influence the relative efficiency of utilization and output of technically trained scientists and engineers. If we could control each of them in such a way as to increase output to the maximum, it is obvious that the effect on the output of our technical brainpower would be tremendous. But it will be some time before we can even approach this ideal state of affairs; most of our knowledge is at the present time sketchy and incomplete. Certainly much further research will be necessary before we can achieve a high level of efficiency in utilizing technical people. But when we finally do manage to do this, a conservative estimate might be that the effective output of the individual scientist or engineer would be doubled. This would mean a further doubling of our technical-brainpower resources above that achievable by diminution of our educational attrition alone.

Seventeen

OUR ULTIMATE BRAINPOWER
POTENTIAL

What are our ultimate brainpower resources?

We could have twice as many scientists and engineers if we were to eliminate the factors which produce the heavy educational attrition among that segment of our population which is capable of completing a college education in engineering and science. Our resources could be doubled again if the technical occupations were made available and attractive to women and if they were encouraged to enter these occupations. These two increases would give us four times our current output without infringing on the needs of other professions. Finally, if we were to utilize our trained manpower in the most efficient manner, and if we were to apply more effort toward increasing its creative productivity, our brainpower output would be doubled again, giving us altogether an eightfold increase in total output. Our total potential output of technical brainpower is, then, about eight times our actual current output.

Earlier, we made the observation that both the yearly production and the total supply of engineers and scientists in the United States has increased tenfold every half-century since 1800, and we asked whether this could be achieved again in the next half-century—from now to the year 2000. Apparently, the answer is almost. As far as the United States is concerned, we can achieve nearly one more tenfold increase in our technical-brainpower output and this could perhaps be the final one.

It is important to recognize that this increase can be achieved without diversion of qualified students from other equally necessary and important occupations. Our calculations assume no increase in the *proportion* of college graduates who obtain degrees in engineering and science. We have assumed that the proportion (22 per cent) of graduates in science and engineering which has held for the past thirty years will remain constant to the end of the century.

It is also important to note that our supply of working scientists and engineers cannot continue indefinitely to grow at an ever increasing rate, as it has in the past. The curve of numbers of scientists and engineers is leveling off as we approach more closely the full utilization of our potential supply. Once we have fully tapped the potential resources by the methods discussed earlier, it will be possible to expand our supply only as populations increase—unless, of course, we change some of the factors which are involved. Thus it is possible that the proportion of students who choose technical vocations might increase. Or we might import our talent from other regions.

In Europe, as in the United States, technical manpower is in short supply. Western Europe, with a population of 154 million, has 425,000 scientists and engineers of all levels of education. The United States, with a population of 168 million, has 760,000. All the considerations which apply to the situation in the United States apply also to that in Europe. In addition, however, we must consider the different attitudes toward universal education in the United States and in Europe. It is generally agreed in the United States that it desirable for about 30 per cent of each age group to complete college. In contrast, higher education in Europe is for the select few, and only about 5 per cent of each age group completes college. Free education for each individual up to the limit of his intellectual ability would greatly increase the production of scientists and engineers in Europe today.

The situation in the Soviet Union is quite different from that in either Western Europe or the United States, and provides an interesting comparison with our own procedures. The Russian system of public education is systematically organized and controlled to meet the needs of the state. Education is highly regarded. Russian young people are motivated to progress as far up the educational ladder as they are able, since the higher one goes, the more privilege and prestige he can attain, and the better the occupation for which he is qualified. Admission from one level of education to the next is by competitive examination. School expenses are borne by the state, and, in addition, some students are subsidized while they attend school. Higher education for the Russian student strongly stresses the technological fields as well as medicine, agriculture, and teaching. About half of all college graduates are in these fields, and of these over 60 per cent specialize in engineering and in the natural sciences.

The Soviet Union badly needs scientists and engineers in order to keep her industrialization program moving at a rapid pace. As a result, her educational system is organized to maximize the output of scientists and engineers at the expense of other fields of intellectual activity. By the time a student has graduated from high school he has completed six years of biology, five years of physics, four years of chemistry, and four years of mathematics. By comparison, our high-school graduates who want to enter science as a career complete two years of biology, one year of physics, one year of chemistry, and three years of mathematics. At the college level, the Russian youth who can gain admission to a technical school is considered very fortunate, for if he can complete this education he will join one of the most privileged classes in Russia today. As a scientist or engineer, he can have a car, a private apartment, a large income, and a position of high status and prestige.

In a sense the Russians have put into effect many of the procedures which we have previously discussed as influencing the production and utilization of engineers and scientists in the United States. The Soviet Union is an example of what can be accomplished if an entire educational system is controlled and geared to the production of as many scientists, engineers, physicians, and teachers as possible, to the near exclusion of other fields, such as the humanities, law, business, and commerce.

As a result of her concentrated effort, the Soviet Union has rapidly overtaken the United States and is currently producing more than twice as many scientists and engineers as are we. It appears probable too that this gap will widen for some time to come. In addition, while only two-thirds of our engineers and one-third of our scientists go to work in their respective fields, all of the Russian scientists and engineers do so for the simple reason that they are told where to work. Also, as we noted earlier, about one-third of Russian technologists are women. The rate at which scientists and engineers are being produced in the Soviet Union suggests that were any nation willing to take similarly drastic steps—to institute rigid controls and to minimize the importance of the non-technological areas of intellectual activity—the output of scientists and engineers would greatly exceed that projected earlier in this book, but at a considerable cost in freedom.

In assessing the potential technical-brainpower resources of the underdeveloped parts of the world, we can use the same line of reasoning we have employed in our analysis of the United States. This is possible because, to the best of our knowledge, the distribution of intellectual ability described for the United States (Figure 26) is the same in principle for all peoples. The races of mankind appear to possess essentially equal mental endowment. This means that between one-third and one-half of all people in any nation or race are potentially capable of doing the kind of thinking and learning that is required in schools of higher education.

There are, of course, social, cultural, and economic conditions which make it improbable if not impossible that at present these peoples could produce college graduates in such quantity. The intangible fruits of intellectual accomplishment are not discernible to primitive societies or to those whose whole effort must be concentrated on the immediate bare necessities of food and shelter. But the potential is there. And so, theoretically, there are great reservoirs of untapped intellectual resources throughout the world. While we are running into short supply in the United States and Western Europe, there is a very large supply in the world as a whole.

If India, with her population of 360 million, were to produce scientists and engineers at the rate which we have calculated as the maximum possible for the United States today (four times our present production), she would produce 450,000 each year. This is almost equal to the number of working engineers and scientists with bachelors' degrees in the United States at the present time.

Obviously the potential technical-brainpower resources of the world are very great. But of course as other countries industrialize, the amount of intellectual work to be done will multiply very rapidly. We in the United States might be able to import intellectual talent from abroad. This would be only a temporary expedient, however, for a time will come when this talent will be required in the countries in which it originates. For the very long-range future, as the United States now carries on a high level of industrialization with its own supplies of technical manpower, so too the world as a whole may carry on a high level of industrialization with world supplies of technical manpower.

Eighteen

THE LONG VIEW

In principle man has at his disposal ample material resources to permit him to provide adequately for a much larger population than exists today and for a very long period of time. The future, viewed solely from the technological standpoint, would appear to offer little excuse for starvation, for privation, or for misery. We know that more food can be produced, that more homes can be built, that more clothing and medicines can be provided. Our physical resources are adequate to provide all these things far into the future.

Yet we also know that to provide an abundant life for all the world's people will undoubtedly prove to be extremely difficult. We have already examined one of the major social difficulties—that of creating the vast reservoir of technical brainpower which will be necessary if the multiplicity of technological problems that will confront us is to be solved in time. But this is only one of the numerous and extraordinarily difficult problems which will demand solution—with disaster as the penalty for failure.

Even were the world completely at peace, with neither war nor the threat of war demanding a substantial fraction of our efforts, the future would be hazardous enough. But in addition men now have in their possession destructive weapons of great power—bombs capable of obliterating the largest cities and quantities of radioactivity capable of destroying human life over entire continents. It seems quite possible that another major war might mean the end of industrial civilization.

An industrial society is probably far more vulnerable to disruption than many of us suspect, composed as it is of a highly complex network of mines and factories, all linked directly and indirectly one to the other by a vast communications system. In such an array the complete destruction of a few key component parts could cause the entire system to cease functioning. And once it has ceased to function, the means for its repair are also removed, so that there may be little opportunity to bring the network into operation again in time to avert mass starvation and death. In a highly industrialized society people are completely dependent upon the smooth functioning of the industrial network for their food, for their medicines and vaccines, indeed for their very survival. The smooth functioning of the network is in turn dependent upon the balanced production of a multiplicity of goods—the proper sizes of nuts and bolts, steel plates and tubing, the necessary vacuum tubes and instruments, the essential chemicals. Were the key units to be suddenly destroyed, the entire system might well collapse.

Indeed, a society such as that of the United States is far more vulnerable to disruption than is an agrarian society such as that of India. Most of the people of India live in small villages, each an independent economic unit producing most of the necessities of life. Cloth is woven, simple tools are manufactured, and food is produced in the surrounding countryside. Were the major cities of India to be destroyed, it would be a long time before some of the villages would hear about the catastrophe, let alone be seriously affected by it.

Nevertheless the underdeveloped areas of the world are themselves rapidly becoming vulnerable to disruption, for the reason that they are becoming increasingly dependent upon certain Western products for continued low mortality. Were a country such as Ceylon suddenly to find that she could no longer obtain DDT, for example, the resultant epidemic of disease would cause a burst in death rate which would almost certainly be disastrous. And as the new inexpensive techniques for control of disease spread still further, to larger countries such as India and China, the vulnerabilities of these areas to disruption will in turn grow.

It is thus becoming increasingly important that war be avoided. But unfortunately, as high-grade resources become depleted in one part of the world after another and as the process of industrialization in underdeveloped areas continues, the avoidance of war may prove to be increasingly difficult. In the first place, increasing competition for the world's remaining high-grade resources can precipitate war. We have seen again and again that threats to a nation's access to critical raw materials, such as oil, can lead to violence.

But even more important is the fact that industrialization and the ability to wage war go hand in hand. In order to wage war today a nation must either herself possess a vast technology, or she must in some way be provided with the products of such a technology. As time goes by, and as the process of industrialization continues, more and more nations will possess the capacity to wage war—to manufacture for themselves mechanized equipment, guns, planes, and nuclear weapons. Japan and the Soviet Union are the two most recent nations to join the group of industrial powers, and we have seen the dangerous situations that have been created by them as they have gained the power to wage large-scale modern war. What will happen as other countries, such as India and China, achieve this power?

One important aspect of the dangers which confront us is concerned with the understandable impatience of people to improve their lot. The process of industrialization is a slow one when viewed in terms of the length of a human lifetime. A doubling time of between five and ten years for industrial production represents a very rapid rate of growth. Yet even under conditions of such rapid development a considerable span of time is required for the average individual to notice much improvement in his life. One reason for this is that the products of industry at first must be diverted largely to the creation of new industry. Machines must be built which can be used to produce other machines. Production of consumer goods must be minimized. In economic terms, there must be "savings," the creation of capital, with the result that the consumer's lot is not rapidly improved. The delay in the arrival of visible economic benefits to the average person can lead, particularly in the mushrooming cities, to discontent and violence.

The slow rate at which food production can be increased within the framework of our existing abilities aggravates the situation still further. We have seen that it is possible to grow enough food on the earth's surface to support the growing population of the world for the next fifty years—and this merely by doing more intensively things we already know how to do. In principle, too, it is possible, through extending our agriculture by procedures which we now regard as uneconomical, to produce sufficient food to support the growing population through perhaps the next century. But unfortunately, although there is no barrier in principle to feeding a far larger number of persons than now exist in the world, the fact remains that it is difficult to increase the amount of food produced each year as rapidly as the number of people is likely to increase. Thus, unless it is possible in some way to slow down birth rates or to speed up production rates, we are faced with the prospect of watching industrialization spread to areas where people are hungry today and are destined to remain hungry for a long time in the future.

A further danger is that the people of underdeveloped countries may be driven by their impatience and by the example of the Soviet Union to totalitarianism, in the belief that by so doing they will be able to accelerate rates of savings and rates of both industrial and agricultural growth. This has already happened in China. India, by contrast, is attempting to carry out an industrialization program within a framework of democratic principles and with an economic system which is in part socialist and in part under private control. As India's industrialization progresses, as her population grows, as people become hungrier, as discontent and impatience increase, one wonders whether democracy will be able to withstand the intense forces which will arise and which can potentially destroy it. In this day when democracy can be replaced by totalitarianism almost overnight, the reverse process is slow, painful, and all but impossible, so powerful are the tools of persuasion and coercion which are available to modern rulers.

If we are able in the decades ahead to avoid thermonuclear war, and if the present underdeveloped areas of the world are able to carry out successful industrialization programs, we shall approach the time when the world will be completely industrialized. And as we continue along this path we shall process ores of continually lower grade, until we finally shall sustain ourselves with materials obtained from the rocks of the earth's crust, the gases of the air, and the waters of the seas. By that time the mining industry as such will long since have disappeared and will have been replaced by vast, integrated, multipurpose chemical plants supplied by rock, air, and sea water, from which will flow a multiplicity of products, ranging from fresh water to electric power, liquid fuels, and metals.

As man approaches this phase of his culture he may well reach a point of no return—a point in time beyond which a major disruption to the world-wide industrial network would be irreversible. Originally the spread of industrialization was facilitated by the fact that man was able to find easily vast beds of iron ore and coal, rich crystals of copper, huge deposits of petroleum, sulphur, and a variety of useful substances. But, as we have seen, these deposits will one day be gone. Our technology will permit us to continue without them for as long as industrial civilization keeps functioning. But if for any reason disaster strikes and the industrial network is destroyed, it seems doubtful that we shall ever again be able to lift ourselves above the agrarian level of existence. The resources which would be required to reactivate the processing of rock and sea water, to reactivate the elaborate interlocking components of an intricate industrial society, might well be far greater than could be commanded. Imagine, for example, that the power needed to reactivate the industrial network must come from a nuclear power plant, and that this must be fabricated and put into operation without benefit of coal, oil, or fuels other than those obtainable from rock. In the absence of adequate available energy it would even be difficult to use the remnants of the industrial civilization. With time, even the technology would be forgotten and would tend to disappear. The people of the Middle Ages used for new buildings the marble facings of the older Roman buildings, but for centuries Roman engineering techniques were in large measure forgotten. The contrast in the future can be an even greater one.

The problems which we face in the years ahead are indeed both numerous and grave, but, theoretically at least, it seems likely that they can be solved by the proper application of our intelligence. For example, some of the dangers which confront us can be relieved by strengthening the international institutions which are designed to prevent war, such as the United Nations and its subsidiary organizations. Others can be decreased if we apply ourselves to the task of reducing our own vulnerability to disruption. Still others can be minimized by concerted effort on the part of the present industrialized countries to enable the inevitable industrial transition of the underdeveloped areas to be made with minimum difficulty. This can be done in part by the transfer of capital and in part by technical aid. It can be promoted also by the development of new techniques in industry, agriculture, education, and birth control—techniques which have not thus far been developed in the West because they have not been needed, but which would be of value to countries that are in the process of development.

In the last twenty-five years we have just begun to build up a body of information on how to assist the underdeveloped areas in increasing their food supplies. We are beginning to understand some of the bottlenecks and limiting factors involved in increasing agricultural output. We have seen that agricultural production is increasing slowly because it involves the education of large numbers of people and the changing of their ideas, prejudices, and cultural values. These characteristics are difficult to change. We badly need to achieve a better understanding of how to spread modern agricultural technology rapidly—of techniques for encouraging the farmers of underdeveloped areas to accept new knowledge.

Similarly, new techniques for control of human fertility could be of value in accelerating economic growth. As in the case of agriculture, however, the main bottleneck in the adoption of techniques of birth control is likely to lie less with the technology than with the necessity for changing people's beliefs. Nevertheless, a substantial decrease in the birth rate could contribute significantly to the rate of economic development and would be equivalent to increases in rates of agricultural and industrial production. In the long run, of course, it is clear that if people desire to maintain low death rates— if they persist in using the techniques of death control—they must match these death rates with equally low birth rates. This means that they must make use of techniques of birth control. The sooner these techniques are adopted on a wide scale, the more rapidly can hunger and privation be eliminated from the world.

When we take the very long view of man's world in the next century we see that the main problems are less those of technology than they are those of men's getting along with other men, communicating with other men, and organizing themselves in such a way that their genius and imagination can be vigorously applied to the problems that confront them. Our major problems involve the enriching, enlarging, improving, and mobilizing of our intellectual forces.

Behavioral scientists are just beginning to uncover some of the principles of human behavior. This knowledge will undoubtedly grow in the years ahead, and as it grows it can be used to rear healthier children and to help adults achieve their full potentialities. We can look forward to the development of better theories of human behavior which will be more precise predictors of future behavior than the theories we have at the present time. Our knowledge of the nature of creative thought processes, of imagination, and of intuition will increase. More knowledge of group dynamics, of social and political behavior, and of means for controlling feelings and emotions can help man achieve his constructive, socially helpful goals and divert him from hostile, destructive action.

As this new knowledge and understanding accrues, a larger and larger percentage of adults will become capable of significant intellectual achievement. But can the necessary information concerning both man's behavior and the physical and biological world about him be accumulated rapidly enough to enable him to cope with the problems as they arise? Can man take the necessary action in time to maintain an ever more complicated industrial network? Can man learn to control his feelings and impulses before they lead him to destruction? These are the key questions.

We have seen that, in principle, man can, if he wills it, create a world where people can lead lives of abundance and creativity within the framework of a free society. It is apparent that there will be many difficulties; there will be many dangers. But it seems reasonably clear what man must do in order that the path may be negotiated. It remains to be seen whether he will recognize these problems in time and proceed to create a still higher level of integration, or whether he will permit his civilization at its present stage of development to disintegrate, perhaps never to reappear. The future of industrial society revolves around the question of whether man can learn to live with man.

NOTES

Since World War II a number of books have appeared on the general subject of man in relation to his resources. Those of most general interest are: F. Osborn (1948 and 1953),[1] Vogt (1948), Hansen (1951), Rosin and Eastman (1953), Ordway (1953), Brown (1954), Bates (1955), Sax (1955), and Meier (1956). To this series should be added the report, *World Population and Resources*, which was prepared in England by PEP (1955). In addition a number of studies have appeared which have brought together a wealth of data concerning man and his resources. Notable among these are the report of the President's Materials Policy Commission (1952), Woytinsky (1953), and Dewhurst (1954).

Several attempts have been made in recent years to take rather long-range looks at man and to forecast his future. Among those of general interest are those of Seidenberg (1950), Darwin (1953), Brown (1954), and Thomson (1955). To these should be added the papers presented at a symposium which was held in 1955 on the general subject of "Man's Role in Changing the Face of the Earth," edited by Thomas (1956).

---

[1] Full listings of the books referred to in the Notes will be found in the Bibliography, listed alphabetically by authors.

2. On Forecasting the Future

For a discussion of the general subject of forecasting the future, see Sir C. G. Darwin (1956). The most readily available edition of Malthus's essay is in "Everyman's Library." This is based on the seventh edition. Bonar (1924) gives a highly readable discussion of Malthus and his times. For an interesting account of possible future technological developments see Thomson (1955). Sir C. G. Darwin discusses the time scale in human affairs in Thomas (1956).

3. Some Contrasts

Facts and figures in this section were derived primarily from Woytinsky (1953), Dewhurst (1954), and conventional statistical references such as the *Minerals Yearbook*, the *Monthly Statistical Bulletins of the United Nations*, and the *Statistical Abstracts of the United States*.

For a discussion of the spread of industrial civilization, see Chapter I of Brown (1954) and the references therein.

4. Demands for Raw Materials in an Industrial Society

Per capita quantities of coal and iron produced in England in the eighteenth and nineteenth centuries are based upon figures given by Woytinsky (1953). Recent levels of per capita consumption in the United States have been derived from the *Minerals Yearbook* and other conventional statistical sources. Some typical values are shown in the tables on page 157.

Values of steel production are higher than those of pig iron, since a large amount of steel is made from reprocessed scrap.

The per capita amount of steel in use in the United States was estimated on the basis of the following assumptions: 1) The average life of end-products containing steel is 20 years—i.e., 20 years elapse from the time an object is manufactured until it is returned to the steel mill as scrap. 2) About 10 per cent of the iron which is put into a steel furnace as a charge is lost irrecoverably. 3) Iron which is not converted to steel is irrecoverably destroyed, on the average, through corrosion and other losses in approximately 100 years. The estimates of about 9 tons per person in use today and somewhat over 8 tons per

Per Capita Consumption of Metals in the United States (1954)

	POUNDS PER PERSON PER YEAR
Steel (1955)	1290
Aluminum	22
Manganese	21
Copper	15
Lead	14
Zinc	11
Nickel	1.2
Tin	1.0
Antimony	0.15

Per Capita Consumption of Non-Metals in the United States (1953)

	POUNDS PER PERSON PER YEAR
Stone, sand, and gravel	9500
Cement	640
Common salt	260
Phosphate rock	175
Lime (other than for cement)	120
Gypsum	105
Sulphur	72
Potassium salts	22
Pyrites	16

person in use in 1950 are only slightly at variance with estimates made by the American Iron and Steel Institute of 7.3 tons per person (1948) and 10 tons per person (1952).

The quantities of metals consumed per ton of steel produced have been computed on the basis of figures obtained from standard statistical sources such as the *Minerals Yearbook*. A few examples are given on page 158.

The estimates of the quantities of copper, lead, and zinc in use are very rough and are based on production figures, estimates of irrecoverable losses, and known rates of scrap recovery.

Pounds of Metals Consumed in the United States
per Metric Ton of Steel Produced

YEAR	COPPER	LEAD	ZINC	TIN	ALUMINUM
1900	39	54	13	6.6	0.5
1920	33	33	24	5.1	4.3
1940	40	26	25	5.8	8.5
1950	42	32	24	3.3	22
1954	40	25	20	2.3	48

For an interesting discussion of the copper situation see Volume II of the report of the President's Materials Policy Commission (1952).

The data for energy consumption in the United States, shown in Figures 3 and 4, were obtained from Ayres and Scarlott (1952), Woytinsky (1953), Putnam (1954), and the *Statistical Abstracts*.

5. TECHNICAL MANPOWER IN AN INDUSTRIAL SOCIETY

A discussion of the changes in the occupational level and distribution of skills in the United States labor force for the period 1900 to 1950 is given in *Scientific American* (September 1951).

The survey of the shortage of scientists and engineers in industrial research was prepared by the United States Department of Labor for the National Science Foundation and published in July 1955. At the time the survey was conducted, in late 1954, shortages of technical personnel were most acute in aircraft, primary metals, electrical equipment, petroleum, paper, food, and scientific-instrument industries. Within engineering, shortages were greatest in the chemical, electrical, mechanical, and aeronautical fields. Among the sciences, the greatest needs were in chemistry, physics, metallurgy, and mathematics.

6. RATES OF INDUSTRIALIZATION

Discussions of reserves of ores can be found in the report of the President's Materials Policy Commission (1952) and in Woytinsky (1953).

Figures showing the growth of steel production were obtained from Woytinsky (1953) and from the *Minerals Yearbook*.

Facts and figures concerning India's program of industrialization and her resources have been obtained from issues of the *Eastern Economist*, New Delhi; from the *Hindu Weekly Review*, Madras; and from numerous publications of the Government of India.

7. WORLD POPULATION

Birth rates, death rates, and population have been discussed at some length in recent years by many authors. Of most general interest are the books of Barnett (1950), Cook (1951), Bates (1955), and the revised edition of Dublin and Lotka (1949). Thompson (1953) is an excellent textbook on population problems.

Population figures can be found in Woytinsky (1953) and in the *Demographic Yearbook* of the United Nations.

Other discussions of population growth can be found in Putnam (1953), Brown (1954), Meier (1956), and in the report of PEP (1955).

Himes (1936) gives a fascinating account of the history of the development and use of contraceptives. Henshaw (1955) gives an authoritative discussion of the future possibilities of fertility control.

For a detailed account of the demography of a single underdeveloped region, see the study by Davis (1951) of India and Pakistan. For more popular accounts of three critical areas (Ceylon, Japan, and Egypt), see Blacker (1956), Rumbold (1956), and the *Population Bulletin* issue on Egypt (1956). PEP (1955) gives vital statistics and brief demographic studies of a number of important areas.

For histories of medicine and public health the reader is referred to Sigerist (1944), Stern (1941), and Winslow (1952).

The vital statistics for England and Wales which are summarized in Figure 8 can be found in PEP (1955).

The postwar increases in fertility among college graduates in the United States are discussed in the annual *College Study Reports* of the Population Reference Bureau. Since 1946 the Reference Bureau has each year surveyed the fertility of college graduates in the United States. Discussion of the broader aspects of the recent increases in fertility in the West can be found in PEP (1955).

The rapidity with which population forecasts can become erroneous is well illustrated by the recent demographic patterns in the United States. In 1952 the President's Materials Policy Commission

estimated that the population of the United States might reach
192 million persons by 1975. This estimate was made about 1950 for the
purpose of guiding estimates of needs in resources. So rapidly did
the population increase between 1950 and 1954 that the United States
Census Bureau estimated that the United States population might reach
200 million by 1970. In 1956 the Census Bureau estimated that by
1965 the United States population might lie between 186 million and
193 million—in other words that we would reach the level assumed by
the Materials Policy Commission some ten years earlier than forecast.

The phenomenal decline of mortality in underdeveloped areas is
discussed by Kingsley Davis in two papers, both published in 1956. He
averaged the percentage decline of crude death rates in eighteen underdeveloped countries in recent years and found the following figures:

PERIOD	AVERAGE PERCENTAGE DECLINE FROM PREVIOUS PERIOD
1925–29	6.0
1930–34	4.6
1935–39	6.3
1940–44	8.5
1945–49	15.2
1950–54	20.1

A few of the more rapid rates of natural increase of population
given by Davis are:

COUNTRY	AVERAGE NATURAL INCREASE PER THOUSAND PER YEAR, 1950–54
Costa Rica	37.3
Formosa	35.0
Mauritius	33.0
Malaya	29.6
Mexico	28.7
Ceylon	27.8
Puerto Rico	27.6

8. World Food Production

Much material for this and the following two sections is taken from the annual summaries of the United Nations Food and Agriculture Organizations, reports entitled *State of Food and Agriculture*. Further general material has been taken from Woytinsky (1953) and the United Nations *Statistical Summaries*. The world's food problems have been considered in detail by Salter (1948), Quisenberry (1948), Bennett (1954), Russell (1954), Brown (1954), Sax (1955), and Meier (1956), among others.

The data for Figure 10 are for average intakes of whole countries and are not based on distribution of intakes of population within each country. Dietary intakes are as of 1952–53. The data are principally from the *State of Food and Agriculture* (FAO, 1954).

The data for Table I are modified from Bonner and Galston (1952). The photosynthesis figures are for net increment after respiration. The calculations as to numbers of people supportable are based on total caloric content of the plant material without regard to digestibility.

Animals are inefficient converters of plants to food for human beings. The grazing animal does not eat the roots, for example, nor does it eat all the leaves, seeds, and stalks. The animal fed on grain does not eat the stalks, roots, leaves. We assume that 0.67 of the plant is consumed. Corn constitutes about 0.33 of weight of the corn plant. Only 50 per cent more or less of the energy content of forage is available to (i.e., digestible by) the grazing animal, while 65 per cent to 80 per cent of the energy content of grain is available. The average percentage conversion of digestible (to the animal) plant food calories to edible (to the human) animal products for the United Kingdom was 9.4 per cent in 1945 (Russell, 1954). We assume that two-thirds of animal calories are supplied as forage and one-third as feed. Of 100 units of plant material,

66 units given as forage $\times$ 0.67 $\times$ 0.5 = 22.4 units for animal
34 units given as feed $\times$ 0.33 $\times$ 0.75 = 8.4 units for animal

Of 100 total units of plant material, 30.8 are available to animal. And 30.8 units converted to animal products for the human diet with an average efficiency of 9.4 per cent, yield 2.9 units of actual food for human beings.

The data for cultivated acres in Figure 11 include cropped, improved pasture, and fallow but not unimproved pastures. The data are principally for 1950 from the United Nations *Statistical Yearbook* (1951) and from Russell (1954). Calories per day per acre are based on total caloric yield of crops divided by total acreage. Thus the contribution from pasture processed through the animal is neglected. This introduces an appreciable underestimate for the United States and Western Europe particularly. The yield data are principally from Russell (1954) and *State of Food and Agriculture* (FAO, 1954 and 1955). The estimate for the USSR is from *World Food Survey* (FAO, 1946). Our other estimates are in general agreement with those of the *World Food Survey*.

The data for original calories per person in Figure 12 are derived from the data of Figure 11. The calories of animal products are derived by calculation from dietary-intake data of the United Nations *Statistical Summary* (1951) and *State of Food and Agriculture* (FAO, 1955). The latter are data for 1952–53. They indicate an apparent conversion of original calories to animal product calories with an efficiency of 14 per cent. This is higher than is actually the case because the contribution of unimproved pasture to the original calories fed to animals has been neglected, since no data are available.

The fertilizers considered in Table II are nitrogen, phosphorus, and potassium. The weights given are the sum of actual nutrient contents of N, P_2O_5, and K_2O. The data are principally from *State of Food and Agriculture* (FAO, 1955). A good summary of fertilizer matters is to be found in Jacobs (1953).

In this section mention is made of the relation of mechanization to agricultural productivity. We know that productivity per farmer is high in the United States, where the farmer has available a plentiful supply of energy to supplement his own, and that productivity per farmer is low in cultures in which the farmer must provide most of the energy himself. The following analysis shows, however, that the energy output in the form of farm products depends on the total energy put into the operation rather than on the form in which the energy is applied.

The figures are for prewar United States and prewar Japan, taken from Woytinsky (1953).

Total Energy Input per Day (Calories)

| | PER FARM WORKER | | PER ACRE | | OUTPUT (CALORIES) |
COUNTRY	HUMAN	SUPPLE-MENTARY	HUMAN	SUPPLE-MENTARY	OF FARM PRODUCE PER ACRE PER DAY
United States	350	4950	10	140	4000
Japan	350	100	420	120	13,000

As the preceding table shows, the United States farmer expends almost 5000 calories per day in addition to his own energy. The Japanese farmer expends only 100 calories per day in addition to his own. But farms in the United States are bigger than in Japan, so that more total energy is expended on an acre of Japanese farm land than on an acre of United States farm land.

The following table summarizes the energy efficiencies of farming in the two regions. This efficiency is nearly the same, since in the United States we obtain about 27 calories of potential food per calorie of energy expended in farm work, while in Japan 24 calories of potential food are harvested for each calorie expended.

Let us look at the efficiency of food production per unit of human energy expended. From this point of view the United States farmer is thirteen times as effective as the Japanese. Note, however, that the Japanese farmer uses his supplementary (non-human) energy more efficiently than does the United States farmer. The latter may run around more.

Output of Food Calories per Calorie of Energy Input

COUNTRY	HUMAN ENERGY	SUPPLEMENTARY ENERGY	TOTAL ENERGY
United States	400	29	27
Japan	31	108	24

The data for Figure 13 are taken from the report of the Japanese Ministry of Agriculture and Forestry for 1955.

The data for Figure 14 are taken from the *Yearbook of Agriculture,* (US Department of Agriculture, 1954). The average production over the period 1935–39 is taken as 100 per cent.

There has been much discussion concerning the area of potentially cultivatable land on the earth's surface. Salter (1948) has estimated that 1 billion acres of tropics and 300 million acres of northern soils can ultimately be cultivated. This has been questioned by Stamp (1952) and others. We assume that of the 1.3 billion acres of tropical and northern lands which are potentially usable but difficult to cultivate, one-third may be actually used. There are in addition 1.3 billion acres of marginally arable land now in pasture, of which a portion is subject to more intense utilization.

For the calculations of Table III it is assumed that acreage of all Asia is increased from 787 million acres to 1000 million acres; the acreage of the rest of the world, from 1610 million acres to 2500 million acres; further, that the acreage of Asia is used to feed Asia, and that of the balance of the world to feed it. It is assumed that a 3000-calorie-per-day European diet requires 6600 original calories, while an Asian diet of 3000 calories per day requires 3500 original calories. A more detailed analysis is:

Potentially Supportable Population (in Billions)

	EUROPEAN DIET		ASIAN DIET	
	3000 CALORIES PER DAY	2500 CALORIES PER DAY	3000 CALORIES PER DAY	2500 CALORIES PER DAY
European level of productivity				
In Asia (1 billion acres)	1.1	1.3	2.0	2.4
In rest of world (2.5 billion acres)	2.7	3.2	5.0	6.0
Japanese level of productivity				
In Asia	2.0	2.4	3.8	4.5
In rest of world	5.0	6.0	9.4	11.4

9. New Knowledge and New Food

For our analysis of the problem of protein production (Table IV) we consider only land actually cultivated to crops in the United States, where the level of productivity for such land is 6250 calories per acre per day. We assume distribution among crops appropriate for conversion to steer or cow. The caloric efficiency of conversion of feed to steer carcass, edible portion, is between 3 per cent and 7 per cent (Brody, 1945) or 7 per cent (Russell, 1954). For conversion to milk it is about 30 per cent if we do not include the food the cow eats while growing to the productive age. Approximately 25 per cent of the calories of the milk are contained in the protein. It is assumed that 67 per cent of all calories of the beef are contained in protein. The soybean and alfalfa yields are average yields. Alfalfa contains about 20 per cent protein, and it is assumed that 75 per cent is recovered in digestible form by appropriate extraction of the plant.

The yield data for Table V for Holland are taken from Wassink (in Burlew, 1953), those for Denmark and the United Kingdom from Russell (1954). They are in general agreement with average yields for these two regions.

Wassink (in Burlew, 1953) has summarized data on actual measurements of the efficiency of crop plants as solar converters, obtaining values of 1.9 per cent to 2.2 per cent for sugar beet, corn, sugar cane, and of 1.2 per cent for potato. These figures apply to the production of the entire plant. The portion of the entire plant which is available as food is summarized below for some typical crops.

		AVAILABLE AS FOOD
CROP	PORTION OF PLANT	PERCENTAGE OF DRY WEIGHT OF WHOLE PLANT
Wheat	Grain	28
Oats	Grain	32
Rice	Grain	34
Corn	Grain	36
Potato	Tuber	75
	Starch of tuber	56
Sugar beet	Root	78
	Sugar of root	55

Let us consider in more detail the factors that limit production of plant material. Why is it that yields, after initial rapid increases, level off as they have done in Japan? We have seen that low crop yields can be increased by addition of fertilizers, by application of water when there is too little, and by the elimination of pests. Each crop plant has, too, its characteristic temperature requirements and grows best in only a limited range of temperatures. Much of the success of plant improve. ment through plant breeding probably is due to matching of plant and climate. When the limitations of water and nutrient have been removed, and when a plant has been selected whose temperature requirements match the region, there are still the limitations imposed by the efficiency with which plants convert solar energy to chemical energy. Green plants, as we know them, can, under optimal climatic conditions and in the absence of other limiting factors, convert and store about 2 per cent of the energy they receive from the sun (Table VII). The energy thus trapped is used not only for the formation of the edible portion of the plant but for the formation of the leaves, stems, roots, and other inedible portions. An over-all efficiency of 2 per cent in conversion of solar energy to plant product has been achieved with our best cultivated crops—sugar cane in the tropics, sugar beet in temperate regions, and probably wheat and rice. This means that of the light energy falling upon the field during the period of cultivation of the crop, 2 per cent is trapped in chemical form. The yield of food for man is determined by the proportion of the plant which is edible—about 30 per cent for cereals; about 50 per cent to 60 per cent for sugar beet or potato. A certain amount of vegetative structure, of roots, stems, and leaves, is necessary to support and maintain the photosynthetic apparatus and to gather nutrients from the soil. The structural materials, cellulose and related compounds as well as lignin, are largely indigestible by human beings but constitute at present an essential 40 per cent to 70 per cent of the plant's substance. It would be of interest to know how far this can be reduced. The cells of algae such as Chlorella are similar in structure and composition to the cells of leaves.

The conversion of solar energy values of Table VII are based upon the amount of light energy which actually fell upon the plant surface as determined by measurement. Clouds reduce this amount below the maximum possible. Only about half of the sun's energy in the spectral region (4000 to 7000 Angstroms) used by plants ordinarily reaches the earth during the six warmest months of the year in the agricultural regions of the temperate zone. It is clear, then, that crop yields under otherwise optimal conditions will necessarily be less in cloudy regions than in sunny regions. This is no doubt one reason why yields of crops are higher in irrigated (and less cloudy) regions.

TABLE VII. *Efficiency of Energy Conversion by Crop Plants*

CROP	REGION	PORTION OF PLANT	CALORIES PER ACRE (MILLIONS)	PER-CENTAGE EDIBLE	PERCENTAGE OF CONVER-SION OF IN-CIDENT LIGHT
		Actually measured (after Wassink, 1953)			
Potato	Holland	Whole plant	14.3	—	1.23
		Tubers	10.7	—	0.92
		Starch of tubers	8.0	56	0.69
Sugar beet	Holland	Whole plant	24.0	—	2.2
		Sugar	13.0	55	1.2
Corn	United	Whole plant	19.0	—	2.2
	States	Grain	7.0	—	0.8
		Digestible part of grain	6.1	32	0.7
Sugar cane	Java	Whole plant	49.5	—	1.9
		Sugar	27.2	55	1.06
		Estimated from yields and average values for light energy			
Rice	Japan	Whole plant	19.1	—	2.2
		Grain	6.5	34	0.75
Wheat	Denmark	Whole plant	16.0	—	2.0
		Grain	4.5	28	0.56

It is of interest to use data on maximum possible solar energy to calculate the upper limit of yields which might be obtained by conventional agriculture—that is, assuming an energy efficiency of 2 per cent. Such calculations indicate that, under optimal conditions in the northern temperate regions and with cloudless skies, yields per acre of 6 tons of sugar, 100 to 135 bushels of wheat, and 150 to 220 bushels of corn should be obtainable. They indicate too that shading by clouds to 50 per cent of full light brings the yield expected on the basis of energy balance down to the levels already attained by our best farmers today. From this point of view, we are already pushing the upper efficiency limit of production of food edible to human beings by our conventional crop plants.

Once we have brought our crops up to this highly efficient limit, what can we then expect? It is possible to double or perhaps more than double crop production per unit area by enrichment of the air above the plants with carbon dioxide in addition to that already contained in the air. This is practicable only with crops grown within closed spaces, as in a greenhouse, or with algae grown in tanks. In these cases efficiency of light conversion by plants can be increased to perhaps 5 per cent, or two and one-half times that obtained in the open.

The second way of increasing over-all light-energy conversion by plants is by the development of crops which grow and capture light for longer periods of the year. Any measures taken for the development of plants capable of growing earlier in the spring and longer in the fall would increase the length of time over which light energy can be captured and would thus increase total yields per acre.

The third question as to what limits ultimate crop yield concerns the problem of whether the 2-per-cent capture of solar energy by green plants at the prevailing CO_2 concentration in the air is fixed by the plant's whim or whether it is already determined by selection at a value which maximizes yield. This question needs to be explored. No ready answer can be given to it at present.

The technology of production of edible yeast, especially valuable for its high protein content, is considered in detail by Meier (1956).

The present status of the world's irrigation agriculture and the prospects for increasing this area by conventional projects are discussed by Thorne and Peterson (1949). A brief survey of the most recent programs is contained in the FAO summary for 1955. Water problems of the United States are thoroughly discussed in the 1955 *Yearbook* of the United States Department of Agriculture. A thorough discussion of the problems of reclamation of sea water is given by Ellis (1954), and the rising water costs in the United States are considered by McKee (1955).

The extensive literature on the cultivation of Chlorella is well summarized in the book edited by Burlew (1953). A more enthusiastic view of the prospects for the cultivation of algae than the one presented in this book is held by Meier (1956).

10. PATTERNS OF AGRICULTURAL CHANGE

The data for Figure 15 are taken from Dewhurst (1955). The fact that real per capita farm income in the United States is now 40 per cent of that of the industrial worker is taken from the FAO report, *State of Food and Agriculture*, for 1955.

11. WHAT IS A RESOURCE?

The view that almost any material in the earth's crust can be looked upon as a potential resource if we are given adequate supplies of energy is discussed at greater length in Brown (1954) and in Meier (1956).

12. OUR ENERGY RESOURCES

Figures for coal, oil, and natural-gas consumption in the world can be found in Ayres and Scarlott (1952), Putnam (1953), and Woytinsky (1953). Figures 16 and 17 were obtained from Hubbert (1956). Factors for converting natural gas and petroleum to equivalent tons of coal are those used by Woytinsky (1953).

Hubbert (1956) has summarized the present situation with respect to fossil-fuel resources, and we have used herein the quantities listed in his paper. The value of 2500 billion metric tons of coal was obtained from a recent report of the United States Geological Survey and was based in part upon the results of older surveys and in part upon new estimates. The main reason for the fact that this figure is between one-third and one-half that of earlier figures is that an attempt has been made to include in the estimate only those seams which can be practically mined. Further allowance was made for losses in mining.

Hubbert uses the values obtained by L. G. Weeks of the Standard Oil Company of New Jersey for the amount of petroleum which might eventually be extracted from the ground, but corrects them for recent findings. The estimated world potential of 1250 billion barrels includes offshore deposits.

For any curve of the consumption of a resource of finite extent we know that consumption must start at zero (when consumption begins), and that it must end at zero (when the resource is exhausted). At some time it must then reach a maximum and begin quickly, or after some time, to decline, depending upon the nature of the uses which caused the consumption.

In view of the fact that we have in the past consumed coal and petroleum at constantly increasing rates, with the percentage of increase itself continuously rising, and probably shall continue to do so for some time in the future, it is likely that the curves of consumption of these two resources will drop very sharply after they have reached the point of maximum use. Hubbert has demonstrated that the time at which we reach maximum consumption is not influenced greatly by our estimates of total reserves. He shows that if we assume the total initial reserve of petroleum in the United States to be 150 billion barrels, we might expect to pass through our peak of production between 1960 and 1965. On the other hand if we assume that the petroleum available is one-third more, or 200 billion barrels, the maximum is postponed only six years.

13. New Knowledge and New Energy

The possibilities of utilizing energy sources other than fossil fuels are discussed by a variety of authors. The reader is referred particularly to Ayres and Scarlott (1952), Putnam (1953), Brown (1954), Ayres (1955), Meier (1956), and to papers by Ayres, Brown, and Scarlott in Thomas (1956).

The most useful discussion of the possibilities of producing power from solar energy is that of Meier (1956). He gives a detailed analysis of the possibility of producing power by cultivating algae. For a discussion of silicon solar-energy converters, see Prince (1955).

For discussions of the potential applications of nuclear energy, the reader is referred to the studies of the National Planning Association, two of which have thus far appeared. The first (Mason, 1955) is a discussion of the relationships between energy requirements and economic growth. The second study (Sapir and Van Hyning, 1956) discusses the potential applicability of nuclear energy in Japan. A third study, on India, is being prepared by Norman Gold and will appear in 1957.

The reader is also referred to the numerous contributions to the International Conference on the Peaceful Uses of Atomic Energy, which was held in 1955 in Geneva. For general discussion we recommend the papers by W. K. Davis, Hill and Joslin, Jukes, Lane, Mayer, and a paper prepared by the staff of the United Nations. Applicability in specific areas is discussed by Aki (Japan), Blokhintsev and Nikolayev (USSR), and Cockcroft (United Kingdom). The potentialities of nuclear energy are also discussed in the publications of the United States Joint Congressional Committee on Atomic Energy.

The importance of foreign exchange and economic self-sufficiency as incentives for the development of nuclear power are discussed in the publications of the National Planning Association. An excellent summary of these aspects of the nuclear-energy problem was given by Philip Mullenbach at the Denver Research Institute–Atomic Industrial Forum which was held in Denver, Colorado, in June 1956.

Figure 20 was reproduced from Hubbert (1956).

The energetics of isolating uranium from granite is discussed by Brown and Silver (1955).

14. TECHNICAL MANPOWER, PRESENT AND FUTURE

The most complete analysis of the supply and demand of college graduates in the United States is contained in Wolfle (1954). The National Science Foundation reports (1955 and 1956) contain data on the supply, utilization, and training of scientists and engineers. DeWitt (1955) has compiled a comprehensive report on the Russian educational system and the production of Soviet professional manpower. A report of the United States Joint Congressional Committee on Atomic Energy (1956) discusses briefly the educational systems in seventeen countries of Western Europe. It includes figures on the production of and demand for scientists and engineers. Excellent bibliographies on technical education and scientific manpower are contained in Cole (1955) and in Weislogel and Altman (1952). For the most recent information on technical-manpower training, utilization, supply, and demand, see the *Engineering and Scientific Manpower Newsletter* published monthly by the Scientific Manpower Commission, Washington, D.C.

Figures on college-graduation trends in the United States are from Oxtoby, *et al* (1952), and from Goldstein (1956). The figure of 11 per cent for 1950 does not include World War II veterans. The estimate of 17 per cent by 1970 is derived from Oxtoby. The proportion of college graduates obtaining degrees in engineering and science was estimated from Wolfle (1954), Appendix tables B.1 and B.2.

Estimates of the proportions of engineers and scientists working in their respective fields of specialization were derived from Wolfle. His data were obtained from a study of persons who graduated from the University of Michigan and from Ohio State University in 1930, 1940, and 1951. A weighting procedure was employed to approximate the age distribution of all living college graduates.

A part of the loss of scientists results from their entering other professional fields at the graduate level. In addition, 25 per cent of science majors go into the health fields and 25 per cent of them enter occupations having little direct relationship with science (business and commerce, 7 per cent; law, 1 per cent; administration, 3 per cent; non-professional, 6 per cent; supervisors, 3 per cent; clerical and sales workers, 2 per cent; manual workers, 1 per cent). Fourteen per cent leave the labor force altogether. The engineers who leave engineering are similarly distributed over a wide diversity of occupations (business and commerce, 10 per cent; law, 1 per cent; other fields, 2 per cent; non-professional, 15 per cent; sub-professional supervisors, 6 per cent; clerical and sales, 3 per cent). Five per cent leave the labor force.

Figures for the curve of future supply of engineers and scientists are based on graduation figures through 1953 and on estimates to the year 2000. Sources used include Goldstein (1956), and Oxtoby, et al (1952). The estimated numbers of future graduates in engineering and science assumes an 11-per-cent increase in the number graduating each decade.

Retirement age was taken to be 65, and losses due to death were derived from mortality figures given by the *Statistical Abstracts of the United States* (1952, Table 83).

The National Science Foundation (1955) reports that among 11,600 companies which were chosen to be representative of American industry, "about 157,000 scientists and engineers—nearly three out of every ten in the surveyed industries—were engaged full time in research and development work in January 1954."

According to Ewell (1955), research and development expenditure has had a growth rate of 10 per cent per year since 1920. On the assumption that this rapidly rising curve might level off in the future, and in order to be on the conservative side, a yearly increase of 6 per cent was used in constructing Figure 23. This is the lowest yearly increase reported since 1920. For a discussion of research and development expenditures, see Bureau of Labor Statistics *Bulletin No. 1148* (1953), Ewell (1955), National Science Foundation (1956).

Wolfle (1954) provides adequate figures for the production of scientists and engineers receiving bachelors' degrees in the United States for the period 1900–1950. He indicates a production of 475,000 engineers and 609,000 scientists for the half-century. Burritt (1912) analyzed the occupations of graduates from 37 colleges for the period 1800–1900. He estimated a production of 1800 engineers in the period 1800–1850, and 22,000 in the period 1850–1900. No figures are available for the production of scientists for these periods. We have assumed that the increase by approximately one-third each decade which was found for 1900–1950 also held for 1800–1900, giving an estimate of 10,000 scientists produced in 1800–1850, and 80,000 in 1850–1900. The total number of engineers and scientists produced in these half-centuries, then, was as follows:

PERIOD	NO. OF ENGINEERS AND SCIENTISTS
1800–1850	11,800
1850–1900	102,000
1900–1950	1,084,000

15. The Production of Scientists and Engineers

See Hollinshead (1952) and Wolfle (1954) for an extensive discussion of college attendance and attrition. The early identification of science students is discussed in Brandwein (1955), Fehr (1953), Mac-Curdy (1954), Roe (1952), and Terman (1954).

Patterns of traits and abilities of different occupational groups are described in Roe (1956) and Terman (1954). See the section by Havighurst and Rodgers in Hollinshead (1952) for a discussion of some of the social, psychological, and cultural motivations which influence college attendance; see also Mulligan (1951) and Havighurst (1948). The need for vocational guidance in high school is discussed by Ginzberg, *et al* (1951), and by Roe (1956). See also Mallinson, Greisen, and Van Dragt (1952). For figures on the science-teacher shortage, see The Fund for the Advancement of Education *Bulletin No. 2* (1955), National Education Association (1956), and National Education Association Research Division (1956).

The Educational Testing Service report on mathematics teachers also states, "Nearly one-third of the states will license them [high-school teachers of mathematics] even though they have had no college mathematics at all, and the average requirement for all is only ten semester hours." T. M. Stinnett (1956) takes issue with this statement and presents teacher-certification data indicating that the states referred to in the preceding statement issue blanket certificates and leave the policing of the number of credit-hours in mathematics to the employing school officer. The median requirement of the states is eighteen hours in professional education. The median requirement for the forty-five states and territories with prescriptions for subject-matter semester hours is eighteen.

The Early Admissions program is described by the Fund for the Advancement of Education (1953).

A discussion of women in the technical fields in the United States is contained in the United States Department of Labor *Bulletin No. 253* (1954), in Michels (1948), and in Weeks (1955). The proportion of women among professionals in the Soviet Union is given in DeWitt (1955):

	PERCENTAGE OF WOMEN		
PROFESSION	*1929*	*1940*	*1951* *
Engineering	14.7	19.4	
Agricultural	9.2	24.4	
Socio-economic	8.2	26.1	
Educational	21.0	37.0	
Health	47.2	56.9	
Total percentage	23.5	32.6	50.5
Total number	68,000	277,000	830,000

* The breakdown for 1951 is not available.

The present percentage of women professionals in different occupational fields is not available. DeWitt states that the proportion of women holding advanced degrees is undoubtedly less than 20 per cent.

16. INCREASING OUR BRAINPOWER OUTPUT

For data and a discussion on technical manpower utilization, see National Manpower Council (1952), (1953), and (1954), and Trytten (1952). Doober and Marquis (1956) contains discussions by several authors on communications and organization. For a discussion of incentives and rewards for scientists and engineers, see Shapiro (1953), Terman (1955), Brandwein (1955), Moore and Renck (1955), and Roe (1952). Brainstorming is described in Osborn (1953).

17. OUR ULTIMATE BRAINPOWER POTENTIAL

Figures and discussion of technical-manpower supplies in Western Europe are contained in the report of the Joint Committee on Atomic Energy (1956). For extensive figures and discussion of Russian technical education and manpower supplies, see DeWitt (1955) and the Joint Committee on Atomic Energy (1956).

10. STRATEGY FOR THE SUPERPOWERS

For this and a discussion on technical change should be a free and global superpower. Connor (1981), (1981) and (1984), and Freedan (1975), Draper and Marston (1984), contains discussions by several authors on some military and organizations for a discussion of the economic and society for families and employer. See Snyder (1975), Trainor (1985), Barnett (1985), Moore and Rose (1983), and Rose (1982). Brinkmanship is discussed in Osgood (1963).

11. OUR DIGITAL SUPERPOWER TOPICS

Figures and discussion of military of manpower supplies in Western Europe are contained in the report of the Joint Committee on Nuclear Energy (1976). For extensive figures and discussion of Russian technical education and manpower supplies see DeWitt (1961) and the Joint Committee on Atomic Energy (1956).

BIBLIOGRAPHY

Aki, Koichi. "Japan's Energy Utilization, the Present and the Future." United Nations International Conference on the Peaceful Uses of Atomic Energy (1955), paper no. 8/P/1060.

American Iron and Steel Institute. *The Picture Story of Steel*, 1952.

———. *Steel Facts*, 1948.

Ayres, E., and Scarlott, C. *Energy Sources, the Wealth of the World*. New York: McGraw-Hill Book Co., 1952.

Ayres, Eugene. "Energy Resources for the Future." *Mines Magazine*, July 1955, p. 39.

Barnett, Anthony. *The Human Species*. New York: W. W. Norton & Co., 1950.

Bates, Marston. *The Prevalence of People*. New York: Charles Scribner's Sons, 1955.

Bennett, M. K. *The World's Food*. New York: Harper & Bros., 1954.

Blacker, C. P. "Japan's Population Problem." *The Eugenics Review*, April 1956, p. 31.

Blokhintsev, D. I., and Nikolayev, W. A. "The First Atomic Power Station in the USSR and the Prospects of Atomic Power Development." United Nations International Conference on the Peaceful Uses of Atomic Energy (1955), paper no. 8/P/615.

Bonar, James. *Malthus and His Work*. London: George Allen & Unwin, Ltd., 1924.

Bonner, J., and Galston, A. W. *Principles of Plant Physiology*. San Francisco: Freeman, 1952.

Brandwein, Paul F. *The Gifted Student as Future Scientist*. New York: Harcourt, Brace & Co., 1955.

Brody, S. *Bioenergetics and Growth*. New York: Reinhold, 1945.

Brown, Harrison. *The Challenge of Man's Future*. New York: Viking Press, 1954.

————, and Silver, L. T. "The Possibilities of Securing Long Range Supplies of Uranium, Thorium and Other Substances from Igneous Rocks." United Nations International Conference on the Peaceful Uses of Atomic Energy (1955), paper no. P/850.

Burlew, J. S. *Algae Culture—from Laboratory to Pilot Plant*. Washington: Carnegie Institution (Publication No. 600), 1953.

Burritt, Bailey. *Professional Distribution of College and University Graduates*. Washington: US Bureau of Education (Bulletin No. 19), 1912.

Cockcroft, Sir John. "The Contribution of Nuclear Power to United Kingdom and World Energy Resources up to 1975." United Nations International Conference on the Peaceful Uses of Atomic Energy (1955), paper no. 8/P/389.

Cole, Charles C. *Encouraging Scientific Talent, A Report to the National Science Foundation*. New York: College Entrance Examination Board, 1955.

Cook, Robert C. *Human Fertility*. New York: William Sloane Associates, 1951.

Darwin, Sir Charles Galton. "Forecasting the Future." *Engineering and Science* (California Institute of Technology), 19:7 (April 1956), p. 22.

————. *The Next Million Years*. New York: Doubleday & Co., 1953.

Davis, Kingsley. "The Amazing Decline of Mortality in Underdeveloped Countries." *The American Economic Review*, May 1956, p. 305.

————. *The Population of India and Pakistan*. Princeton: Princeton University Press, 1951.

————. "The Unpredicted Pattern of Population Change." *The Annals of the American Academy of Political and Social Science*, May 1956, p. 53.

Davis, W. Kenneth. "Capital Investment Required for Nuclear Energy." United Nations International Conference on the Peaceful Uses of Atomic Energy (1955), paper no. 8/P/477.

De Castro, J. *The Geography of Hunger*. Boston: Little, Brown & Co., 1952.

Dewhurst, J. F. *America's Needs and Resources*. New York: The Twentieth Century Fund, 1954.

De Witt, Nicholas. *Soviet Professional Manpower*. Washington: National Science Foundation, 1955.

Doober, M. J., and Marquis, Vivienne. *Effective Communication on the Job*. New York: American Management Association, 1956.

Dublin, L., and Lotka, A. J. *Length of Life*. New York: Ronald Press, 1949.

Dyer, H. S., Kalin, R., and Lord, F. M. *Problems in Mathematical Education*. Princeton: Educational Testing Service, 1956.

Ellis, C. B. *Fresh Water from the Ocean*. New York: Ronald Press, 1954.

Ewell, Raymond. "Role of Research in Economic Growth." *Chemical & Engineering News*, 33:29 (1955), p. 2980.

Fehr, Howard F. "General Ways to Identify Students with Scientific and Mathematical Potential." *The Mathematics Teacher*, vol. 46, April 1953, p. 230.

Food and Agriculture Organization (FAO). *Food and Agriculture. World Conditions and Prospects*, 1949.

———. *State of Food and Agriculture*, 1953, 1954, 1955.

———. *World Food Survey*, 1946.

Fund for the Advancement of Education. *Bridging the Gap between School and College*. (Evaluation Report No. 1.) New York, 1953.

———. *Teachers for Tomorrow*. (Bulletin No. 2.) New York, 1955.

Ginzberg, Eli, *et al. Occupational Choice*. New York: Columbia University Press, 1951.

Goldstein, Harold. "Recent Trends in and Outlook for College Enrollments." *Monthly Labor Review* (US Dept. of Labor, Bureau of Labor Statistics), March 1956.

Haber, W., Harbison, F., Klein, L. R., and Palmer, G. L. *Manpower in the United States: Problems and Policies*. New York: Harper & Bros., 1954.

Hanson, E. P. *New Worlds Emerging*. New York: Duell, Sloan & Pearce, 1951.

Havighurst, Robert J. "Social Implications of the Report of the President's Commission on Higher Education." *School and Society*, vol. LXVII (April 1948), p. 257.

Henshaw, Paul. *Adaptive Human Fertility*. New York: McGraw-Hill Book Co., 1955.

Hill, J. M., and Joslin, S. W. "The Capital Investment for Nuclear Energy." United Nations International Conference on the Peaceful Uses of Atomic Energy (1955), paper no. 8/P/391.

Himes, N. E. *A Medical History of Contraception*. Baltimore: Williams & Wilkins Co., 1936.

Hollinshead, Byron S. *Who Should Go to College?* New York: Columbia University Press, 1952.

Hubbert, M. King. *Nuclear Energy and the Fossil Fuels*. Houston, Tex.: Shell Development Co., Exploration and Research Division, 1956. (Publication No. 95, to be published by the American Petroleum Institute in *Drilling and Production Practice*.)

Jacobs, K. D. (ed.). *Fertilizer Technology and Resources*. New York: Academic Press, 1953.

Japanese Ministry of Agriculture and Forestry. *Annual Report*, 1955.

Jukes, J. A. "The Cost of Power and the Value of Plutonium from Early Nuclear Power Stations." United Nations International Conference on the Peaceful Uses of Atomic Energy (1955), paper no. 8/P/390.

Lane, James A. "Economics of Nuclear Power." United Nations International Conference on the Peaceful Uses of Atomic Energy (1955), paper no. 8/P/476.

MacCurdy, Robert D. *Characteristics of Superior Science Students and Some Factors That Were Found in Their Development*. Boston: Boston University, 1954 (doctoral dissertation).

Mallinson, G. G., and Van Dragt, H. "Stability of High School Students' Interests in Science and Mathematics." *School Review*, LX:6 (September 1952), p. 362.

Malthus, T. R. *An Essay on the Principle of Population*. "Everyman's Library"; London: J. M. Dent & Sons, Ltd., 1914.

Mason, Edward S. *Energy Requirements and Economic Growth*. Washington: National Planning Association, 1955.

Mayer, K. M. "The Economic Potential of Nuclear Energy." United Nations International Conference on the Peaceful Uses of Atomic Energy (1955), paper no. 8/P/475.

McKee, J. E. "Looking Ahead for Water." *Engineering and Science*

(California Institute of Technology), 19:24 (October 1955).

Meier, Richard L. *Science and Economic Development.* New York: John Wiley, and Massachusetts Institute of Technology, 1956.

Michels, Walter C. "Women in Physics." *Physics Today,* 1:8 (December 1948), p. 16.

Moore, D. G., and Renck, R. "The Professional Employee in Industry." *The Journal of Business,* XXVIII:1 (January 1955), p. 58.

Mulligan, Raymond A. "Socio-Economic Background and College Enrollment." *American Sociological Review* XVI:1 (April 1951), p. 188.

National Education Association. *The Crucial Years, 1955 Annual Report to the Profession.* Washington: National Commission on Teacher Education and Professional Standards, 1956.

———. "The 1956 Teacher Supply and Demand Report." *The Journal of Teacher Education,* March 1956, p. 3.

National Manpower Council. *A Policy for Scientific and Professional Manpower.* New York: Columbia University Press, 1953.

———. *Student Deferment and National Manpower Policy.* New York: Columbia University Press, 1952.

———. *The Utilization of Scientific and Professional Manpower.* New York: Columbia University Press, 1954.

National Science Foundation. *Research and Development by Nonprofit Research Institutes and Commercial Laboratories, 1953.* Washington: US Government Printing Office, 1956.

———. *Science and Engineering in American Industry.* Washington: US Government Printing Office, 1955.

———. *Scientific Personnel Resources.* Washington: US Government Printing Office, 1955.

———. *Trends in the Employment and Training of Scientists and Engineers.* Washington: US Government Printing Office, 1956.

Ordway, Samuel H., Jr. *Resources and the American Dream.* New York: Ronald Press, 1953.

Osborn, Alexander F. *Applied Imagination: Principles and Procedures of Creative Thinking.* New York: Charles Scribner's Sons, 1953.

Osborn, Fairfield. *The Limits of the Earth.* Boston: Little, Brown & Co., 1953.

———. *Our Plundered Planet.* Boston: Little, Brown & Co., 1948.

Oxtoby, T., Mugge, R., and Wolfle, D. "Enrollment and Graduation Trends: from Grade School to Ph. D." *School and Society*, 76:1973 (October 1952), p. 225.

Political and Economic Planning (PEP). *World Population and Resources*. London, 1955.

Population Reference Bureau. "College Study Report—1956." *Population Bulletin*, October 1956.

———. "Egypt's Population Explodes." Ibid., July 1956.

President's Materials Policy Commission. *Resources for Freedom*. 5 vols. Washington: US Government Printing Office, 1952.

Prince, H. B. "Silicon Solar Energy Converters." *Journal of Applied Physics*, vol. 26 (1955), p. 534.

Putnam, P. *Energy for the Future*. New York: Van Nostrand Co., 1953.

Quisenberry, K. S. *Crop Production Potentials in Relation to Freedom from Want*. Waltham, Mass.: Chronica Botanica, 1948.

Roe, Anne. *The Making of a Scientist*. New York: Dodd, Mead & Co., 1952.

———. *The Psychology of Occupations*. New York: John Wiley & Sons, 1956.

Rosin, J., and Eastman, M. *The Road to Abundance*. New York: McGraw-Hill Book Co., 1953.

Rumbold, Richard. "Into the Madding Crowd: Ceylon and Its Population Problem." *The Eugenics Review*, July 1956, p. 87.

Russell, Sir E. J. *World Population and Food Supplies*. London: George Allen & Unwin, Ltd., 1954.

Salter, R. M. *World Soil and Fertilizer Resources in Relation to Food Needs*. Waltham, Mass.: Chronica Botanica, 1948.

Sapir, Michael, and Van Hyning, Sam J. *The Outlook for Nuclear Power in Japan*. Washington: National Planning Association, 1956.

Sax, K. *Standing Room Only*. Boston: Beacon Press, 1955.

Scientific American. "The Human Resources of the U. S." 185:3 (September 1951).

Scientific Manpower Commission. *Engineering and Scientific Manpower Newsletter*, Washington, 1956.

Seidenberg, Roderick. *Post-Historic Man*. Durham: University of North Carolina Press, 1950.

Shapiro, Theresa. "What Scientists Look for in Their Jobs." *Scientific Monthly*, vol. LXXVI, June 1953, p. 335.

Sigerist, H. E. *Civilization and Disease*. Ithaca, N.Y.: Cornell University Press, 1944.

Stamp, L. D. *Land for Tomorrow*. Bloomington: Indiana University Press, 1952.

Stern, B. J. *Society and Medical Progress*. Princeton: Princeton University Press, 1941.

Stinnett, T. M. "Editorial Comments." *The Journal of Teacher Education*, September 1956, p. 1.

Terman, Lewis M. "Are Scientists Different?" *Scientific American*, 192:1 (January 1955), p. 25.

——. "The Discovery and Encouragement of Exceptional Talent." *The American Psychologist*, 9:6 (June 1954), p. 221.

——. "Scientists and Nonscientists in a Group of 800 Gifted Men." *Psychological Monographs*, 68:7.

Thomas, William L., Jr. (ed.). *Man's Role in Changing the Face of the Earth*. Chicago: University of Chicago Press, 1956.

Thompson, Warren S. *Population Problems*. 4th ed.; New York: McGraw-Hill Book Co., 1953.

Thomson, Sir George. *The Foreseeable Future*. Cambridge, England: University Press, 1955.

Thorne, D. W., and Peterson, H. B. *Irrigated Soils*. Philadelphia: Blakiston Co., 1949.

Trytten, Merriam H. *Student Deferment in Selective Service, A Vital Factor in National Security*. Minneapolis: University of Minnesota Press, 1952.

United Nations. *Statistical Yearbooks*, 1951, 1952, 1953, 1954, 1955.

——. "World Energy Requirements in 1975 and 2000." United Nations International Conference on the Peaceful Uses of Atomic Energy (1955), paper no. 8/P/902.

United States Department of Agriculture. *Marketing. Yearbook*. Washington: US Government Printing Office, 1954.

——. *Water. Yearbook*. Washington: US Government Printing Office, 1955.

United States Department of Labor. *Employment Opportunities for Women in Professional Engineering* (Women's Bureau Bulletin No. 253). Washington: US Government Printing Office, 1954.

————. *Scientific Research and Development in American Industry: A Study of Manpower and Costs* (Bureau of Labor Statistics Bulletin No. 1148). Washington: US Government Printing Office, 1953.

United States Joint Congressional Committee on Atomic Energy. *Engineering and Scientific Manpower in the United States, Western Europe and Soviet Russia.* Washington: US Government Printing Office, 1956.

————. *Peaceful Uses of Atomic Energy.* Washington: US Government Printing Office, 1956.

Vogt, William. *The Road to Survival.* New York: William Sloane Associates, 1948.

Weeks, Dorothy. "Women Power Shortages in the Physical Sciences." *Journal of the American Association of University Women,* 48.3 (March 1955), p. 145.

Weislogel, Mary H., and Altman, James W. *Abstracts of Literature Concerning Scientific Manpower.* Washington: Manpower Branch, Human Resources Division, Office of Naval Research, 1952.

Winslow, C. E. A. *Man and Epidemics.* Princeton: Princeton University Press, 1952.

Wolfle, Dael. *America's Resources of Specialized Talent.* New York: Harper & Bros., 1954.

Woytinsky, W. S., and Woytinsky, E. S. *World Population and Production.* New York: The Twentieth Century Fund, 1953.

INDEX